Fitness Science Explained

*A Practical Guide to Using
Science to Optimize Your Health,
Fitness, and Lifestyle*

By Michael Matthews (legionathletics.com) and James Krieger (weightology.net)

Copyright © 2020 Michael Matthews

This book is a general educational health-related information product and is intended for healthy adults aged 18 and over.

This book is solely for information and educational purposes and does not constitute medical advice. Please consult a medical or health professional before you begin any exercise, nutrition, or supplementation program or if you have questions about your health.

There may be risks associated with participating in activities or using products mentioned in this book for people in poor health or with preexisting physical or mental health conditions.

Because these risks exist, you should not use the products or participate in the activities described in this book if you are in poor health or if you have a preexisting mental or physical health condition. If you choose to participate in these activities, you do so knowingly and voluntarily of your own free will and accord, assuming all risks associated with these activities.

Cover designed by Damonza (damonza.com)

Published by Oculus Publishers (oculuspublishers.com)

Also by Michael Matthews

Bigger Leaner Stronger

Thinner Leaner Stronger

Beyond Bigger Leaner Stronger

The Shredded Chef

The Little Black Book of Workout Motivation

Free Bonus Material:
Takeaways, Workout Plans, Research Reviews, and More

THANK YOU for reading *Fitness Science Explained.*

James and I hope you find it insightful, accessible, and practical, and we hope it helps you get fitter, leaner, and stronger faster.

We want to make sure you receive as much value from this book as possible, so we've put together several additional free resources to help you, including:

- A reference guide to save, share, and print, with all of this book's key takeaways, checklists, and action items.
- High-quality exercise and nutrition studies for you to analyze and interpret using the information and methods you'll learn in this book.
- "Best of" issues of the most popular fitness science research reviews, including Monthly Applications in Strength Sport (MASS), Alan Aragon's Research Review (AARR), and Weightology.

- An entire year's worth of evidence-based workouts for men and women, neatly laid out and provided in several formats, including PDF, Excel, and Google Sheets.
- And more.

To get instant access to all of those free bonuses (plus a few additional surprise gifts), go here now:

⇒ fitnesssciencebook.com/bonus

Also, if you have questions or run into difficulties, just shoot us an email at mikem@legionsupplements.com or james@weightology.net, and we'll do our best to help.

Contents

Chapter 1

Good Science, Bad Science: The Difference and Why It Matters

Chapter 2
How to Think About Science

Chapter 3
Welcome to the Hierarchy (of Evidence)

Chapter 4
The Anatomy of Research

Chapter 5
The Anatomy of Statistics

Chapter 6

How to Rapidly Evaluate Research

Chapter 7

The Complete Beginner's Guide to Scientific Journals

Introduction

We live in a society exquisitely dependent on science and technology, in which hardly anyone knows anything about science and technology.

—CARL SAGAN

IN THIS BOOK, you'll learn everything you need to know to read, understand, and apply scientific research to optimize your health, fitness, and lifestyle, and also how to protect yourself against misguided, misleading, and even menacing advice supposedly supported by research.

This book can't deliver the depth of understanding provided by a formal education, but it'll give you a crash course in identifying good and bad science and credible experts and fake gurus.

Furthermore, this book doesn't require that you have any higher learning or background in science or health and fitness. We designed it from the outset to teach you in simple terms what most people will never know about how to understand and evaluate scientific research.

We won't skimp on details, either. We'll cover all of the big moving parts, including the basics of the scientific method to the differences between randomized trials and observational studies, the placebo effect, "blinding," statistical analysis, and more.

In the first section, you'll learn why diet and exercise science seems so confusing and contradictory.

You'll discover how the media sometimes accidentally and sometimes intentionally misinterprets research, how people "cherry pick" data to support conclusions, why quality research is so scarce, and more.

The second section is all about the heart of science: the scientific method.

You'll learn what the scientific method is and what its limitations are, including external validity, sample sizes, animal vs. human research, and more.

In the third section, you'll learn about the different types of studies that can be conducted and why some carry more weight than others.

The fourth section of the book is the meat and potatoes: how to read and understand scientific research.

Here you'll learn the precise definitions of key terminology used in all research, the anatomy of a scientific study and statistical analysis, and how to put it all together and assess the validity of studies, including two sample analyses for you to sink your teeth into.

You'll also get a "cheat sheet" checklist that'll help you quickly and accurately estimate the quality of research you want to review.

In the fifth and last section, you'll learn about scientific journals, including why some are more reliable than others, how to get access to full-text studies (without spending a fortune), and the most popular journals for exercise, nutrition, and supplementation.

You'll also find out how to locate studies on topics you're interested in, whether it's something we've covered or not.

That'll wrap up the book, but it won't be the end of the line for us.

It'll be the beginning, because you'll be ready to take everything you've learned and use science to enhance your health, body composition, physical performance, and any other aspect of your body and life you want to improve.

Before we get into all of that though, let's answer a question you may be asking yourself: "Who are you two and why should I trust you?"

First, our "official" bona fides:

James Krieger is a published scientist with over twenty scientific papers published in journals such as the *Journal of Strength and Conditioning Research, Sports Medicine,* and the *European Journal of Sports Science,* as well as a frequent speaker at academic conferences on advances in health and fitness research.

James also runs the popular Weightology research review (weightology.net), where he analyzes the latest scientific research on building muscle, losing fat, and getting healthy and shows you how to turn it into immediately actionable tactics and techniques.

And I (Mike Matthews) am a bestselling evidence-based fitness author whose books have sold over 1,500,000 copies around the world and helped thousands of men and women lose fat, build muscle, and get healthy, and my work has been featured in many popular outlets including *Esquire*, *Men's Health*, *Elle*, *Women's Health*, *Muscle & Strength*, and more, as well as on FOX and ABC.

I'm also the founder of Legion Athletics (legionathletics. com), which produces all-natural science-based sports nutrition supplements, and the host of *The Muscle for Life Podcast* (muscleforlifepodcast.com), a top-rated fitness podcast that receives over 600,000 plays per month.

In other words, James is one of the most respected, knowledgeable, and experienced fitness scientists in the game, and I'm one of the most respected and successful fitness authors and entrepreneurs, and together, we've created the best book we could on how to use science to get better in just about any way you desire—fitter, stronger, healthier, happier, you name it.

Embracing an evidence-based approach to not just your diet and training but other areas of your life you want to improve can be a game-changer, and we hope this book inspires you to make this quantum leap in your fitness and beyond.

Now, let's talk science.

1

Good Science, Bad Science: The Difference and Why It Matters

The saddest aspect of life right now is that science gathers knowledge faster than society gathers wisdom.

—ISAAC ASIMOV

ONE MONTH, media headlines blazon that research has confirmed that one food or another reduces your risk of cancer, diabetes, obesity, or some other nasty health condition.

Hooray, you think, time to load up on said food!

Then, some time later, after it has become a staple in your meal plans, the other shoe drops: *new* research refutes earlier findings and demonstrates that it actually *increases* your risk of disease and dysfunction.

What the heck? How can scientific research just turn on a dime like that and do a full 180? Oh well, you think, a few months of eating this way can't have been *that* harmful. Life goes on.

Then it happens again. And again. And again. Eventually, you conclude that science can't seem to make up its mind on anything and you stop paying attention.

Fortunately, this isn't true.

It may appear that there's a study to "prove" or "disprove" just about any assertion, but this illusion isn't the fault of science itself, but rather the widespread misunderstandings about the scientific process, media sensationalism, and sometimes even fraudulent research.

Let's take a closer look at the nine main reasons that science can appear to be so confusing and contradictory.

1. Media Misrepresentation

Attention spans are shorter than ever these days, and when news organizations have just a few hundred words or seconds to report on health matters, they can't afford to discuss the nuances of complicated scientific research.

Instead, they need titillating headlines and easily digested soundbites that draw eyeballs and clicks, and bounce around in social media and water cooler conversations. That inevitably leads to misinformation.

The two most common ways this occurs are:

1. Confusing correlation with causation.
2. Oversimplification and sensationalism.

Let's go over each.

Confusing Correlation with Causation

Quite a bit of health-related research is based on observational data, meaning that scientists observe groups of people going about their lives, collect various types of data, and then look for correlations between different variables. (A correlation is a mutual relationship or connection between two or more things.)

For example, it was through observational research that the link between smoking and lung cancer was first discovered. In the famous British Doctors Study of 1954, scientists sent out questionnaires to British doctors asking them about their smoking habits. The scientists then looked at which doctors got lung cancer and found that doctors who reported smoking were more likely to get the disease.

This type of research is a fantastic tool for documenting phenomena, forming hypotheses, and pointing the way for further research, but it can *never* be used to conclusively determine the cause of the phenomena observed because there are many ways for variables to be related without one causatively influencing the other.

For instance, ice cream intake goes up in the summer, as does the incidence of drowning. So, you could say that there's a strong correlation between eating ice cream and drowning.

This does not mean that eating ice cream *causes* people to drown, however, which is how your average media outlet might explain it.

A good example of this is how the media has reported that drinking diet soda can make you fat. Cause and effect, cut-and-dried. These warnings were based on research that showed that people who drank diet soda more often also tended to be more overweight, which may or may not be true.

What if diet soda isn't causing weight gain, but instead, obese people tend to switch to diet soda in hopes of losing weight? That is just one of a number of alternative hypotheses that could explain the correlation, and that's why further, more rigorous research is needed to identify the true cause.

Well, in this case, that additional research has already been done, and scientists found that the correlation between obese people and drinking diet soda was, in fact, due to their efforts to lose weight.[1] In other words, diet soda was more popular among overweight people trying to lose weight because it contains fewer calories than regular soda. Furthermore, when it's used in this fashion (to reduce overall calorie intake), diet soda consumption is associated with weight *loss*, not gain.[2]

Unfortunately, the media makes this type of mistake all the time. Studies show that news outlets tend to report on observational research more than randomized controlled trials, which *can* establish correlation (and which you'll learn more about soon), as well as lower-quality studies that should be taken with a grain of salt.[3]

Oversimplification and Sensationalism

The media will often oversimplify or distort the results of a study to make a nice, catchy, "clickbait" headline. Tim Caulfield of the University of Alberta has coined a term for this: *scienceploitation.*

For example, a popular UK website once ran the headline, "A glass of red wine is the equivalent to an hour at the gym, says new study," with a sub-headline of "New research reveals skipping the gym in favor of the pub is ok."

Perfect, many people thought, *time to exercise less and drink more!*

If you actually read the scientific paper, though, you'll quickly realize that isn't what the study found.[4] Instead, it found that a compound in grapes and red wine called *resveratrol* may increase exercise capacity (how well people or animals tolerate intense exercise) in rats who are already exercising. There was no red wine involved in this study, and it never showed that people should stop working out.

Another example of this is when the media reported on a study from the *New England Journal of Medicine* with headlines claiming that drinking coffee could make you live longer.[5] However, not only did the media make the mistake of confusing correlation and causation, they also failed to mention that the study only involved people who had already lived to at least 50 years of age, had no history of cancer, heart disease, or stroke, and didn't smoke. There were many other limitations to the study as well, which the scientists mentioned in the paper, but the media failed to report on.

Why Can the Media Get Away With This?

There are likely three reasons why this type of reporting continues unabated:

Journalists often have little formal training in science, and thus are unable to ensure their stories are scientifically accurate.

The general public also has little formal training in science, and is thus unable to differentiate good from bad reporting.

Sensationalism sells so there's always an incentive for the media to spin scientific research in sensationalistic ways.

Keep in mind that most of these organizations rely on advertising revenue to survive, and advertising revenue is driven by website visits. Thus, from a business perspective, writing articles that get a lot of clicks is far more important than being scientifically accurate (especially when it would reduce the virality of the content).

2. Cherry Picking Versus Going by the Weight of the Evidence

It's very common to have dozens or even hundreds of published studies on any given topic, and in many cases, the results aren't all in agreement. Sometimes the differing or even contradictory results come from differences in how the studies were designed and executed, sometimes shenanigans are afoot, and sometimes it's just random chance.

This is why scientists consider the weight of the evidence available as opposed to the findings of a single study.

Think of a scale, with one group of studies more or less in agreement on one side, and another group that indicates otherwise on the other side. The scale will favor whichever side has more evidence to support its assertion, which you could say is where the "weight of the evidence lies." Thus, a good scientist will say, "Given the weight of the evidence, this explanation is most likely true."

Unfortunately, due mainly to ignorance, personal biases, and the media's love of controversy, research is often "cherry picked" to make claims that go against the weight of the evidence. In other words, people often pick out and play up studies that they don't realize are flawed, that they just personally agree with, or that will make for great headlines.

A perfect example of "cherry picking" occurs among some of the more zealous advocates of low-carb dieting. They often hold up a few studies as definitive proof that low-carb diets are better for losing fat, and claim there's no room left for discussion or debate. When you peruse these studies, though, you'll find glaring flaws in how they were carried out, and when you collect and analyze *all* of the available research on the matter, you'll find there is no practical difference in fat loss between low- and high-carb diets so long as calories and protein intake are matched.

In other words, so long as people are eating the same amount of calories and protein, the amount of carbohydrate they're eating won't meaningfully impact their fat loss. In the final analysis, dietary adherence, not carb intake, is the biggest predictor of weight loss success.

Thus, a scientist worth their salt would say, the weight

of the evidence indicates that there are no differences in fat loss between low- and high-carb diets so long as calories are restricted and protein intake is adequate. Accordingly, individuals should choose the diet that they can best stick to for maximum results.

(Yup, the old adage is true: in many ways, the best weight loss diet is the one you can stick to.)

3. Different Quality Levels of Studies

As I mentioned above, there are often a large number of studies published on a particular topic, and some are better than others.

There are many factors to consider when assessing the quality of a study, ranging from the type of research (observational or otherwise) it is to how well it's designed, how many participants there were, whether humans or animals were involved, and more. Thus, when you're working to determine the weight of the evidence, you have to consider not only the *number* of studies on each side, but the *quality* as well.

For example, if I have ten studies with only ten subjects each that points to one conclusion as well as two studies with 1,000 subjects each that points to another conclusion, then the weight of the evidence lies with the latter, even though the former conclusion has more individual studies on its side. (As you'll learn later in this book, *sample size*, which is the number of samples measured or observations used in a study, is a major determinant of the quality of research.)

A perfect example of how ignoring the quality of research can result in misleading conclusions is antioxidant supplementation. There's low-quality evidence in the form of observational research and small-scale trials on animals and humans that suggests antioxidant supplementation may reduce the risk of cancer, and high-quality research in the form of randomized clinical trials that shows antioxidant supplementation doesn't.

Guess which research the media and mainstream health "gurus" decided to champion? Yep, the low-quality research, and antioxidant supplements started flying off the shelves.

4. Science Moves Slowly

Contradictions are a natural part of the scientific process. Many conclusions in science are tentative because they're based on the best evidence available at the time.

However, as time moves on, and as scientists accumulate more data and evidence, newer findings and understandings can overturn older ones. This is particularly true when there's little data and evidence to begin with.

A good example of this process is the story of butter versus margarine.

Three decades ago, as evidence accumulated that the saturated fat in butter may be related to heart disease risk, scientists recommended that people switch to margarine to reduce their saturated fat intake.

However, evidence then began to accumulate that the chemically modified fats (trans-fat) in margarine were even worse than saturated fat in regard to heart disease risk. Based on this newer evidence, scientists revised their recommendations to continue to limit butter, but also eliminate margarine and trans fats from diets.

5. Science Often Deals in Shades of Grey Rather Than Black and White

Science is full of nuance and therefore research usually doesn't lend itself well to headlines and soundbites, which is what most people want—simple, neat, black-or-white answers to their questions.

Unfortunately, though, many scientific topics operate more in shades of grey, and especially when the evidence isn't strong. There is often a lot of uncertainty in the realm of science, which the general public finds uncomfortable. They don't want "informed guesses," they want certainties that make their lives easier, and science is often unequipped to meet these demands. Moreover, the human body is fantastically complex, and some scientific answers can never be provided in black-or-white terms.

All this is why the media tends to oversimplify scientific research when presenting it to the public. In their eyes, they're just "giving people what they want" as opposed to offering more accurate but complex information that very few people will read or understand.

A perfect example of this is how people want definitive answers as to which foods are "good" and "bad." Scientifically speaking, there are no "good" and "bad" foods; rather, food quality exists on a continuum, meaning that some foods are *better* than others when it comes to general health and well-being.

Take sugar, a molecule that most people consider "bad." In and of itself, it's not a harmful substance, and one of its components is necessary for life (glucose). Research shows that when it's consumed in moderation as part of a calorie controlled diet, it doesn't cause adverse health effects or fat gain.[6] However, when sugar is added to highly processed foods to enhance their palatability and energy density, these foods become easier to overeat, and the resulting increase in calorie consumption and fat gain can become a health issue.[7]

That doesn't make for a good tweet or "elevator pitch" to a book publisher, though, and so the research on sugar tends to be separated into two buckets: one that shows it's "good" and another that shows it's "bad." This creates the illusion of incongruity, when in fact, it's just a case of missing the forest for the trees.

6. Lack of Reproducibility/Replication

A very important concept in the realm of science is replication, or reproducibility.

For a scientific finding to be considered true, it needs to be reproduced, meaning that other scientists should be able to achieve the same results by repeating the experiment. This is important, because if other scientists can't replicate the results, then it's likely the initial results were a fluke.

The media loves to report on "hot" new studies with new findings, but often such studies are small "pilot" experiments that have yet to be reproduced with larger sample sizes and better study designs. Often, later studies end up refuting the results of the original "breakthrough" research, giving the appearance of conflicting evidence. In reality, the initial results were happenstance. This is why it's important to be cautious when viewing small studies with new or unusual findings.

One of the greatest examples of this happened in the 1980's. Two scientists held a press conference, saying they'd been able to make atoms fuse at room temperature (cold fusion). However, they hadn't reproduced their results, and other scientists weren't able to reproduce the results either. By late 1989, most scientists considered the prospect of cold fusion dead.

It's also important to take note of the labs conducting research. If one lab consistently produces a certain result, but other labs can't reproduce it, then the research coming from the former lab should be viewed with skepticism. For example, one lab has produced astounding muscle-building results with the supplement HMB, but other labs haven't been able to reproduce anything close, which calls the positive results into question.[8,9]

7. Poor Research Design/Execution

Sometimes a study produces unusual results simply because it's poorly designed and executed.

A perfect example of this is research out of the Ramazzini

Institute in Italy that supposedly showed that aspartame caused cancer in rats.[10] The research was heavily criticized by leading scientific organizations for having many flaws, including the fact that the control rodents had unusually high cancer rates, and the fact that when independent scientists asked to double check the data, the Institute flat out refused.

In most cases, organizations like this are outed among the scientific community, but by that time the story has already made its way through the media cycle, convincing many that once again, the scientific process doesn't make any sense.

8. Unpublished Research

When scientists do a study, they collect the data, analyze it, write up the results, and submit the write-up to a scientific journal for publication.

The study then goes through a process of *peer-review*, which consists of other independent scientists reviewing it for flaws. Based on their findings, the study is either accepted for publication or rejected.

The peer-review process isn't without flaws, but it's the first line of defense against bad research getting published and then propagated by the media. Thanks to peer-review, if a study is published in a scientific journal, you can at least know it's gone through some type of quality control.

This isn't the case with unpublished research. For example, scientists often present new research at conferences that has yet to be peer-reviewed or published. Sometimes the media catches wind of these reports and runs with them before they've gone through the peer-review process, and sometimes scientists will themselves promote the findings of studies that haven't been peer-reviewed or published.

One case of this was on September 30th, 2011, when Martin Lindstrom reported on his unpublished neuroimaging iPhone study in the New York Times. He reported that people experienced the same feelings of love in response to their iPhones ringing as they did in the company of their partners, best friends, or parents. Many scientists criticized Lindstrom, stating that his data didn't support such a conclusion. But, since Lindstrom had bypassed peer review, his dubious conclusions were all that most people ever heard or saw.

Companies that sell products often report unpublished research as authoritative proof of their effectiveness. You should be wary of such research, because it hasn't been scrutinized by independent scientists, and is often designed and executed in such a way as to guarantee positive results.

For example, the creator of a cold exposure vest claimed that his product could help people burn up to 500 extra calories per day. This startling promise was based on research he conducted himself where people wore the vest for 2 weeks and lost fat.

This trial was never peer-reviewed or published in any scientific journal, and if it had been submitted for review, it would have been rejected for egregious design flaws. For instance, the alleged increase in energy expenditure was based on unreliable estimates of body composition rather than direct, validated measurements of energy expenditure.

9. Fabricated Research

Fabricated research essentially means research that's been made up. While fabricated research isn't nearly as common as everything else we've covered so far, it still exists, and can lead to great confusion.

Scientists may falsify data for a number of reasons, including to gain money, notoriety, and funding for further research, or merely to add another publication to their name. One of the most famous cases of fabricated research came from Andrew Wakefield. In 1988, he published a paper in the prestigious journal *Lancet* that showed an association between the Measles/Mumps/Rubella (MMR) vaccine and autism in children.[11] However, it was later discovered that he had fabricated some of his data; independent researchers discovered that Wakefield's descriptions of the children's medical cases differed from their actual medical records.

Wakefield's paper was eventually retracted from the journal, but to this day, his fraudulent research is still used to support the claim that vaccines may cause autism, despite numerous studies showing no such relationship.

Scientific research can seem like a quagmire of misinformation, contradiction, and outright lies.

When you look under the hood, though, you quickly find that the media selectively picks studies designed to generate the most controversy, spins the findings for maximum dramatic effect, and withholds information about how they were conducted.

In other cases, the shenanigans start before the studies hit your Facebook feed.

Poor study designs skew the results and some scientists accidentally or intentionally falsify their data.

Despite all of that, it's still the best system we have for answering this simple question: What's probably true, and what isn't?

To understand how honest, intelligent researchers go about answering that question, we need to take a closer look at the scientific method.

Key Takeaways

- The media often misrepresents scientific studies by confusing correlation with causation, and oversimplifying and sensationalizing data.
- The media gets away with this because journalists and the public often have little formal training in science, and sensationalism sells so there's always an incentive for the media to spin scientific research.
- It's very common to have dozens or even hundreds of published studies on any given topic, and in many cases, the results aren't all in agreement. Unfortunately, due mainly to ignorance, personal biases, and the media's love of controversy, research is often "cherry picked" to make claims that go against the weight of the evidence. In other words, people often pick out and play up studies that they don't realize are flawed, that they just personally agree with, or that will make for great headlines.
- There are many factors to consider when assessing the quality of a study, ranging from the type of research (observational or otherwise) it is to how well it's designed, how many participants there were, whether humans or animals were involved, and more. Thus, when you're working to determine the weight of the evidence, you have to consider not only the number of studies on each side, but the quality as well.
- Contradictions are a natural part of the scientific process. Many conclusions in science are tentative because they're based on the best evidence available at the time.

However, as time moves on, and as scientists accumulate more data and evidence, newer findings and understandings can overturn older ones. This is particularly true when there's little data and evidence to begin with.

- For a scientific finding to be considered true, it needs to be reproduced, meaning that other scientists should be able to achieve the same results by repeating the experiment. This is important, because if other scientists can't replicate the results, then it's likely the initial results were a fluke.

- Peer-review consists of other independent scientists reviewing research for flaws. Based on their findings, the study is either accepted for publication or rejected. Scientists often present new research at conferences that has yet to be peer-reviewed or published. Sometimes the media catches wind of these reports and runs with them before they've gone through the peer-review process, and sometimes scientists will themselves promote the findings of studies that haven't been peer-reviewed or published.

- Fabricated research isn't common, but it can lead to great confusion. Scientists may falsify data for a number of reasons, including to gain money, notoriety, and funding for further research, or merely to add another publication to their name.

- Despite its many flaws, the scientific process is still the best system we have for answering this simple question: What's probably true, and what isn't.

2

How to Think About Science

*Nothing has such power to broaden the mind as the
ability to investigate systematically and truly all
that comes under thy observation in life.*

—MARCUS AURELIUS

ONE OF THE BIGGEST STEPS you can take toward both
protecting yourself from bad science and benefitting from good
science is learning how the scientific method works.

You know what it is in a general sense—the pursuit of
knowledge, but you probably aren't familiar with the exact
steps that have to be taken to get that knowledge.

Once you understand the primary components of the scientific method, you can appraise "science-backed" claims for
yourself and come to your own conclusions.

Let's start at the top.

What Is Science?

Science is simply a way to think about a problem or set of observations.

We observe something in the world. Then we think, "Hmmm, that's interesting. I wonder why that happens." Next, we come up with ideas as to why it happens and then test them. If our ideas fail the tests, then we test new ideas until something passes, at which point we can confidently say that the passing ideas may explain our original observations.

Basically, the scientific process goes like this:

1. We have a problem or set of observations that needs an explanation.
2. We formulate a *hypothesis,* a proposed explanation for our problem or set of observations.
3. We test the hypothesis using data.
4. If the data doesn't support our hypothesis, then we change our hypothesis and test the new one.
5. If the data supports our hypothesis, we continue to test it using a variety of observations, more data collection, and multiple experiments.
6. If a set of related hypotheses is consistently and repeatedly upheld over a variety of observations and experiments, we call it a *theory.*

Much of science revolves around step #3, the process of hypothesis testing.

Scientific studies are the primary ways in which scientists engage in hypothesis testing, which, contrary to popular belief, doesn't aim to prove whether something is "true," but simply "most likely to be true." You can rarely prove something to be absolutely and universally true, but you can engage in a process of narrowing down what is most likely true by showing what isn't true, and that's science's primary goal.

Hypothesis testing may sound abstract, but you actually do it every day.

Imagine a situation where your TV isn't working. This is step #1 in the above process; you have a problem (you can't watch Game of Thrones). You then formulate a hypothesis as to why the TV isn't working (step #2). In this case, you hypothesize that it might be because it's not plugged in. You then engage in step #3 and test your hypothesis with data. In this case, you check behind the TV to see if it's plugged in. If it isn't plugged in, this can be considered support for your hypothesis. To further test the hypothesis, you plug the TV in and try to turn it on. If it turns on, then you have arrived at the proper conclusion as to why the TV wasn't working.

If the TV still doesn't turn on even if it's plugged in, however, then you've ruled out the plug as the problem. In essence, you've *falsified* your hypothesis that the problem was due to the plug.

You now have to change your hypothesis (step #4) to explain why the TV isn't working. Now you think that maybe it's because the batteries in the remote are dead. This is your new hypothesis, and to test it, you press buttons on the remote and observe that the light on the remote doesn't illuminate when you click the buttons. This *supports* your hypothesis, so you go grab new batteries to put in the remote. In this way, you continue to go through steps 2 to 4, learning what isn't true, until you narrow down the correct reason as to why your TV isn't working.

When testing hypotheses, falsification is more important than support because, as mentioned above, you rarely can prove something to be unequivocally true. Rather, you arrive at the most likely explanation by showing what *isn't* true.

Here's an example to show you what this looks like in action.

Let's say a professor has a classroom full of students, and he takes them through an exercise. He passes out a paper to all of the students that looks like this:

Sequence	Fit Professors' Rule?	Guess Professors' Rule	How Sure?
2,4,6	:-)		_____ %
			_____ %
			_____ %
			_____ %
			_____ %
			_____ %

The professor tells all of his students that he has a rule in his head that can be used to generate number sequences. He gives the first sequence that fits with this rule—the sequence 2,4,6—and puts a smiley face next to it to signify this.

The professor then asks his students to guess the rule and write it on their sheets as well as estimate on a scale of 0-100 percent how certain they are that they're correct. A typical student's sheet might look like this:

Sequence	Fit Professors' Rule?	Guess Professors' Rule	How Sure?
2,4,6	:-)	Counting up by two's	50%

In this case, the student thinks that the rule is "counting up by two's," and she's 50 percent sure this is correct.

The professor then asks his students to generate a new number sequence that they think might fit the rule. After they've done this, the professor draws smiley faces next to the sequences that fit and frowny faces for those that don't. A typical student's sheet may now look like this:

Sequence	Fit Professors' Rule?	Guess Professors' Rule	How Sure?
2,4,6	:-)	Counting up by two's	50%
6, 8, 10	:-)		

In this case, the student wrote "6, 8, 10" as a number sequence, and the professor indicated that it fit the rule.

Again, the professor asks the students to guess the rule, and write how certain they are that they're correct. Now, a typical sheet might look like this.

Sequence	Fit James' Rule?	Guess James' Rule	How Sure?
2,4,6	:-)	Counting up by two's	50%
6, 8, 10	:-)	Counting up by two's	60%

After doing this a number of times, a student's sheet may look something like this:

Sequence	Fit Professors' Rule?	Guess Professors' Rule	How Sure?
2,4,6	:-)	Counting up by two's	50%
6, 8, 10	:-)	Counting up by two's	60%
20, 22, 24	:-)	Counting up by two's	70%
3, 5, 7	:-)	Counting up by two's	80%
25, 25, 29	:-)	Counting up by two's	90%
200, 202, 204	:-)	Counting up by two's	100%

In this instance, the student has tested her hypothesis multiple times and is now 100 percent certain that the rule is "counting up by two's." What about you? Do you agree?

Well, it turns out that the student is wrong—this is *not* the correct rule—and she would've realized this if she had tried to falsify the "counting up by two's" hypothesis. Instead, however, she continued to use number sequences that simply confirmed her belief that the rule was "counting up by two's," which led to a faulty conclusion.

Let's look at how this student could test another number sequence to try to disprove her "counting up by two's" hypothesis:

Sequence	Fit Professors' Rule?	Guess Professors' Rule	How Sure?
2,4,6	:-)	Counting up by two's	50%
10, 20, 30	:-)		

In this instance, the student wrote a number sequence that was NOT "counting up by two's," and received a smiley face. So, the rule isn't "counting up by two's," but perhaps some other variation of counting up. It's time to test a new hypothesis, and she devises "counting up by multiples."

Sequence	Fit Professors' Rule?	Guess Professors' Rule	How Sure?
2,4,6	:-)	Counting up by two's	50%
10, 20, 30	:-)	Counting up by multiples	60%

To test this new hypothesis (counting up by multiples), the student tries to disprove it by putting in a number sequence that is NOT counting up my multiples. Once again, the professor indicates the sequence fits his rule, meaning the student is wrong again and must modify the hypothesis. Now, the student changes it to "counting up by even numbers."

Sequence	Fit James' Rule?	Guess James' Rule	How Sure?
2,4,6	:-)	Counting up by two's	50%
10, 20, 30	:-)	Counting up by multiples	60%
100, 500, 894	:-)	Counting up by even numbers	70%

Correct again, but there's still work to be done—namely, disproving this newest hypothesis of "counting up by even numbers."

Eventually, through repeated testing and falsification, the student discovers the rule: "counting up."

Sequence	Fit Professors' Rule?	Guess Professors' Rule	How Sure?
2,4,6	:-)	Counting up by two's	50%
10, 20, 30	:-)	Counting up by multiples	60%
100, 500, 894	:-)	Counting up by even numbers	70%
1, 9, 20	:-)	Counting up	80%
27, 33, 409	:-)	Counting up	90%
55, 212, 999	:-)	Counting up	100%

In this instance, the student has tested her hypothesis multiple times and is now 100.

As you can see, falsification of hypotheses is a crucial part of discovering what's true and what's not, and that's why it's at the heart of how science works. In real life, scenarios can be far more complicated, but the basic approach is the same.

Scientific research begins with a hypothesis and a set of *predictions* from that hypothesis, which are things that *should* be true, *if* our hypothesis is true. These predictions are then tested by doing experiments and gathering data. If our predictions are shown to be false, then we need to modify our hypothesis or trash it for a new one. If it pans out, then we know that our hypothesis may indeed be true, and if it continues to pan out in further research, we've created a valid *theory*.

So let's say you had a hypothesis that Mike Matthews was Batman (hey, you never know!).

From this hypothesis, you would formulate a set of predictions that *should* be true if Mike and Batman were the same person. These predictions would include:

1. Mike and Batman won't be in the exact same place at the exact same time.
2. Mike will consistently be missing when Batman appears, and vice versa.
3. Batman will most frequently turn up in areas of close proximity to where Mike lives.
4. Mike's and Batman's voices should have similarities.
5. Mike and Batman should be of similar height.
6. DNA testing should produce a match.

Failure of these predictions would indicate that Mike and Batman are not the same individual . . . but we may never be able to know for sure. ;-)

Science works in this exact fashion. We have a hypothesis (X is true). We then develop a set of predictions from that hypothesis (if X is true, then A, B, and C must be true). We then test our predictions with scientific studies. In other words, we do studies to see if A, B, and C are true. If they aren't, then X is not true.

Here's a real life example of hypothesis testing in the fitness world. One popular hypothesis among some people is that carbohydrates make you fat, through the actions of the hormone insulin. We know that eating carbs raises insulin levels, so when you eat a high-carb diet, your insulin levels are generally higher.[12] We also know that insulin inhibits the breakdown of fat for energy and stimulates fat storage, so we can hypothesize that the high insulin levels produced by a high-carb diet will make fat loss more difficult.[1]

The next step is developing a set of predictions from this hypothesis—things that *should* be true, if carbs and insulin actually make you fat. Some of these predictions could include:

1. Obese people should show less fat released from their fat tissue since they have higher insulin levels.
2. High insulin levels should predict future weight gain.
3. Fat loss should increase when we switch from a high-carb diet to a low-carb diet, while keeping protein and calorie intake the same.

There are many other predictions that could be developed from this hypothesis, but let's just focus on these three, which have already been tested in experiments and shown to be false.

*   In one study, obese people show *increased* fat release from their fat tissue.[2]
*   In another, high insulin levels did *not* predict future weight gain.[3]
*   In yet another, fat loss was the same, or slightly less, when people switched to a low-carb diet compared to a high-carb diet with similar protein and calorie intake.[4]

Given the failure of these predictions, we can confidently say that the hypothesis that "carbs make you fat via insulin" is false.

As scientists repeatedly develop hypotheses and test their predictions using research, the hypotheses that aren't true get thrown out, and the hypotheses that are most likely to be true are kept.

Rather, the evidence to support a hypothesis accumulates over time, and the more high-quality evidence that exists to support it, the more true the hypothesis becomes. As mentioned earlier, when a hypothesis or set of hypotheses is supported by a large body of high quality evidence that has withstood rigorous scrutiny through repeated testing, we call it a *theory*.

Given that science is based on the accumulation of evidence, its conclusions are always tentative. In other words, there is no such thing as 100% certainty in science (which is why you can't absolutely prove anything).

Instead, there's a degree of certainty, and that degree is based on how much evidence there is to support a scientific concept. Some conclusions in science may be regarded with a high level of certainty due to the vast amount of supporting data and evidence, and others may be highly uncertain due to the lack of high-quality evidence.

You can imagine scientific research as a form of betting. In some areas of science, the data and conclusions are so strong that you would be willing to bet your life savings on it. In other areas, the data is so lacking that perhaps you might only be willing to bet $100 on it, or not even that.

The importance of accumulated evidence is why reproducibility is so important. For a hypothesis to be true, the experiments that support it should be reproducible by scientists other than those who created it by repeating their experiments and observing the same results. This is also why considering the weight of the evidence is critical when coming to conclusions, and why science tends to move slowly over time.

An example of how conclusions rest on the strength of the evidence is the relationship between blood lipids and heart disease.

While some "pop-science" book authors have tried to question the relationship between blood levels of Low-Density Lipoproteins (LDL) and heart disease, the fact is that this relationship is very strong and is supported among multiple lines of evidence, and the evidence is also very strong that decreasing your LDL levels decreases your risk of atherosclerosis.[5]

Thus, the evidence is overwhelming that elevated LDL causes heart disease; it's the type of evidence you'd be willing to bet your life savings on. Now, it's also been suggested that High-Density Lipoproteins (HDL) are protective against heart disease. However, the evidence for that isn't as strong; while observational studies support a relationship, studies that directly change your HDL via drugs haven't shown any reduction in heart disease risk.[6] Thus, this is the type of evidence that perhaps you might only be willing to risk $100 on.

The Limitations of Science

While science represents our best tool for understanding and explaining the world around us, it isn't without its limitations.

This is particularly true when it comes to exercise and nutrition research, whose limitations include, but aren't limited to:

External Validity

External validity refers to the ability to extrapolate the results of a study to other situations and other people.

For example, equations used to estimate body composition in Caucasians don't apply to African-Americans or Hispanics because the density of fat-free mass is different between different ethnicities.[7]

There are many factors that can limit the external validity of a study. Some research is performed under highly controlled, artificial conditions, some is only performed on certain populations, like individuals with diabetes or other health conditions, and some studies may use protocols that don't reflect what people do in real life.

Sample Size

Many studies in the field of exercise and nutrition have a very small number of subjects (often only 10 to 20 people per group).

This can make it difficult to extrapolate findings to thousands of people because small samples can increase the risk of random findings. For example, as mentioned earlier, small studies suggested that antioxidant supplementation could reduce cancer risk. However, once larger studies came out, it was clear that antioxidant supplementation didn't reduce cancer risk.

Small sample sizes can also make it more difficult to detect small but meaningful changes in certain variables. For example, some studies haven't shown any differences in muscle size between low- and high-volume weight training.

However, these studies had a small number of subjects, and short-term changes in muscle size can be so small that they're hard to detect. This may explain why an in-depth analysis of a number of studies on the topic has suggested that training volume does indeed impact muscle size. [8]

Animal vs. Human Research

Animal studies have an advantage over human studies in that scientists have more control over the environment, activity, and food. This allows scientists to do a better job of isolating the variables they're studying.

However, these studies can be limited in how much you can extrapolate the results to people, because animal physiology, while similar to humans, isn't the same. For example, rodents have a much greater capacity to convert carbs to fat, which means that high- versus low-carb studies in rodents aren't necessarily applicable to people.

Lack of Control in Free-Living People and Inaccuracy of Self-Reporting

Many studies in the realms of exercise and nutrition are done on free-living individuals, that is, people living outside the controlled environment of a laboratory.

These studies are easier to conduct, but they're also challenging because scientists are limited in how much they can control for unknown variables that can change the results. For example, it's been shown that people are notoriously inaccurate when reporting how food much they eat and how physically active they are, and therefore, studies that rely on self-reported food intake or physical activity may not be reliable.[9,10]

Science is a systematic process for describing the world around us. Through the process of hypothesis testing and confirmation or falsification, we can eliminate what definitely isn't true, and hone in on what's most likely to be true.

The beauty of science is that it's self-correcting, and is built on a body of evidence that's accumulated and interpreted over time. It has plenty of limitations, as do individual studies, but that doesn't mean the scientific method or scientific experiments are fundamentally invalid. It just means we have to carefully consider the quantity and quality of evidence on a given matter when determining our level of certainty in our conclusions.

Key Takeaways

- The scientific process goes like this: We have a problem or set of observations that needs an explanation. We formulate a hypothesis, a proposed explanation for our problem or set of observations. We test the hypothesis using data. If the data doesn't support our hypothesis, then we change our hypothesis and test the new one. If the data supports our hypothesis, we continue to test it using a variety of observations, more data collection, and multiple experiments. If a set of related hypotheses is consistently and repeatedly upheld over a variety of observations and experiments, we call it a theory.

- When testing hypotheses, falsification is more important than support because you rarely can prove something to be unequivocally true. Rather, you arrive at the most likely explanation by showing what isn't true.

- As scientists repeatedly develop hypotheses and test their predictions using research, the hypotheses that aren't true get thrown out, and the hypotheses that are most likely to be true are kept. We say "most likely to be true" because science can never prove anything definitively.

- The evidence to support a hypothesis accumulates over time, and the more high-quality evidence that exists to support it, the more true the hypothesis becomes. When a hypothesis or set of hypotheses is supported by a large body of high quality evidence that has withstood rigorous scrutiny through repeated testing, we call it a theory.

- While science represents our best tool for understanding and explaining the world around us, it isn't without its limitations. Four of the most common limitations of exercise and nutrition research are lack of ability to extrapolate the results of a study to other situations and other people, small sample size, reliance on animal research that can't be applied to humans, and lack of control over people in free-living environments.

3

Welcome to the Hierarchy (of Evidence)

If I have seen further than others, it is by standing upon the shoulders of giants.

—ISAAC NEWTON

YOU NOW KNOW how science fundamentally works and the role that evidence plays in the scientific method.

You also know that not all evidence is created equal—there's high- and low-quality evidence, and the ultimate goal of any line of research is the accumulation of high-quality evidence for a given hypothesis.

What determines the "quality" of evidence, though, and why do some kinds of evidence carry more weight than others?

Answering this question can seem all but impossible when you're poking around online. Every time you think you know what a study means, someone else comes along and points out why another, better piece of evidence trumps that one.

The good news is that scientists have a proven system for ranking evidence called the *hierarchy of evidence*. A hierarchy is "a system or organization in which people or groups are ranked one above the other according to status or authority."

Here's how the hierarchy of evidence works, with the highest-quality evidence at the top, and the lowest-quality at the bottom:

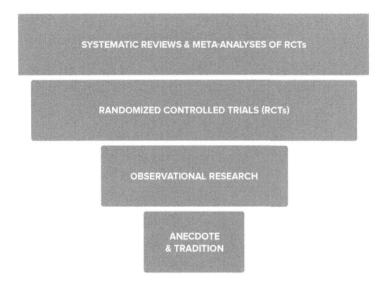

Let's take a closer look at each, starting at the bottom, with the weakest form of evidence.

Anecdote and Tradition

Anecdote and tradition represent the lowest quality of evidence. Anecdote refers to things like "it worked for me" or "my friend got great gains from using this supplement," and tradition refers to things like "everyone does it this way" or "bodybuilders have always trained like this."

These are valid forms of evidence.

The scientific method is relatively new, especially as applied to the fields of health and fitness, so anecdote and tradition are what most people relied on for years.

And it tends to get the basics right.

Ask many experienced bodybuilders and athletes what you should do to get in shape, and most will probably tell you "lift weights, do some cardio, and eat lots of fruits, vegetables, and lean meats."

The problem, though, is that you'll get plenty of conflicting opinions, too. If you only rely on anecdote and tradition to make decisions about what's true and what isn't, then you can waste years second-guessing yourself, jumping from one diet, supplement, and exercise plan to the next.

Sound familiar?

The reason anecdote and tradition are considered low-quality evidence is because there are too many unknown variables and things that aren't controlled.

For example, just because bodybuilders have traditionally trained a certain way doesn't mean it's the best way to train. Many aspects of bodybuilding training are based on ideas that have been passed down from one generation to the next.

People tend to engage in herd behavior, following what everyone else is doing even if it's not necessarily optimal, so there may not be any truth to these things that "everyone knows" about bodybuilding.

Another example is that just because a particular supplement has worked for someone doesn't mean the supplement generally works. Perhaps the psychological expectation that the supplement would work resulted in the person training harder and paying more attention to diet, which would explain the better results. Perhaps the person was simultaneously doing other things that were responsible for the improved gains. Or, perhaps the individual was already improving his body composition and the supplement had nothing to do with it.

As you can see, anecdote and tradition occupy the bottom of the hierarchy of evidence for good reason.

Observational Research

Next on the hierarchy is observational research, which you briefly learned about earlier in this book.

With this type of research, scientists observe people in their free-living environments, collect some data on them, and then look for relationships between different variables. In the world of disease, this type of research is known as *epidemiological research*.

An example of this type of research would be where scientists take a very large group of people (think thousands), assess their dietary habits and body weight, and then review those numbers 10 years down the road. They may look at how many people had heart attacks during that 10 year period, and then use tools to see whether heart attacks could be related to diet.

This type of research is higher quality than anecdote or tradition because the data has been systematically gathered from large numbers of people and formally analyzed. However, as mentioned earlier, it can only establish correlations (relationships), not cause and effect.

For example, you might be able to show that higher fat intake is related to heart attack risk regardless of body weight. That doesn't mean higher fat intake *causes* heart attacks, though, since there are other health variables (like diet and exercise) that can influence that relationship.

Scientists can try to use statistics to reduce the likelihood of other variables skewing the results, but they can never fully isolate one variable as the causative factor in an observational study.

In other words, they can point you in the right direction, but that's about it. That's what these studies are typically used for—justifying more expensive, detailed studies on a particular topic.

And that leads us to the *randomized controlled trial*.

Randomized Controlled Trials (RCTs)

Next, we have one of the highest quality forms of evidence: the randomized controlled trial, or RCT.

In an RCT, scientists take a group of people and randomly divide them into two or more groups (hence the term "randomized"). The scientists try to keep everything the same between the groups, except for one variable that they want to study, which is known as the *independent variable.*

Scientists change the independent variable in one or more groups, and then see how the people respond. One group may not receive any treatment, or may get a fake treatment (also known as a sham treatment or a placebo), and this group is often called the *control group*, hence the term randomized *controlled* trial.

For example, let's say scientists want to see how creatine supplementation affects muscle strength. Here's how the study could go:

The researchers recruit people for the study, and then randomly assign them to a high-dose creatine group, a low-dose creatine group, and a placebo or control group (a group that thinks they're getting creatine but aren't). Before supplementation begins, everyone's strength is measured on a simple exercise like the leg extension, and then all of the subjects do the same weight training program for 12 weeks while also taking the supplement or placebo every day.

After 12 weeks, leg extension strength is measured again and the data is analyzed to see if some groups gained more strength than others. If the changes are significantly greater (more on *significance* soon, as this has a specific definition) in the creatine groups, the scientists can state that the creatine caused greater increases in strength compared to not taking creatine. They can also compare strength gains between the high-dose and low-dose creatine groups to see if a higher dose is more effective.

RCTs rank above observational research because their

highly controlled nature allows them to establish cause and effect relationships. In the above example, assuming the research is conducted honestly and competently, it's scientifically valid to say that that study showed that creatine *causes* an increase in strength gain.

RCTs do have limitations, though. One major factor is the number of subjects involved because, as you know, the smaller the sample size, the higher the risk of random findings. Another is how similar the research environment is to real life. In some cases, the research environment can be so highly controlled that the results might not be applicable to the general population.

For example, many studies that look at appetite have subjects consume food in a lab environment. However, the number of foods and the amounts of food given in the lab can impact how much people eat.[1] Thus, how people eat in the lab may not reflect how they eat in the real world.

By and large, though, a well-conducted randomized controlled trial is the most accurate tool we have for deciding what's probably true and what isn't.

So, what could be better than an RCT?

A bunch of RCTs.

Systematic Reviews and Meta-Analyses of RCTs

When a group of studies exists on a particular topic, a systematic review or meta-analysis can tell you where the weight of the evidence lies on that topic. This is why they occupy the top of the evidence pyramid.

Let's unpack exactly what that means.

A systematic review is a type of study that involves gathering all of the research on a particular topic, and then evaluating it based on a set of predefined rules and criteria. In other words, the research is reviewed in a *systematic* fashion designed to minimize researcher biases.

This is different from a *narrative review*, where a researcher or researchers will informally gather evidence around a topic and share their opinions about what it means.

A meta-analysis is similar to a systematic review, but takes things one step further and does a formal statistical analysis of RCTs. You can think of it as a "study of studies" because scientists gather a bunch of RCTs that fit predefined criteria, and then run complicated statistical analyses on them to give you an idea where the overall weight of the evidence lies.

Systematic reviews and meta-analyses represent the highest level of evidence because they gather the best RCTs and research on a topic and show you what that research generally agrees on.

For example, one systematic review and meta-analysis of weightlifting research looked at 21 studies comparing light loads (<60% 1-rep max) to heavy loads (>60% 1RM) and how those training plans impacted strength and muscle gain.[2]

The analysis showed the gains in strength are greater with heavy loads compared to light loads, but gains in muscle size were similar as long as sets were taken to muscular failure. This type of analysis is superior to any individual study because it produces findings that are more likely to be true for most people.

While systematic reviews and meta-analyses represent the highest level of evidence, they still have flaws. Poor study selection or statistical analysis can lead to poor results because these types of studies are only as good as the data and methods used.

For instance, if you take a bunch of studies with mediocre results, combine them into a meta-analysis, and then run them through the right statistical tools, you can make the results look more impressive at first glance than they really are.

A good example of this is a 2012 meta-analysis on the effects of acupuncture on chronic pain that reported that acupuncture reduced pain 5% more than sham acupuncture (placebo)[3]. When you look at the details, though, you discover that none of the highest-quality studies in the review showed significant effects, and the researchers included several studies with extreme results that were likely the result of bias or flawed research methods, as well as several smaller studies with a higher likelihood of false positive results. Therefore, the study's conclusion that "acupuncture is effective for the treatment of chronic pain" was misleading and oversold.

You've probably asked yourself at one time or another, "With all of the conflicting studies out there, how are you supposed to know what's true and what's not?"

Now you know the answer—by examining how robust evidence is according to the hierarchy, you can understand which claims are more likely to be true than others.

You can know, for instance, that anecdotes online or even published case studies shouldn't be weighted more than the results of RCTs, that the results of an individual RCT aren't the final word on a matter, and that research reviews and meta-analyses can be scientific treasure troves.

Key Takeaways

- Scientists have a proven system for ranking evidence called the hierarchy of evidence. A hierarchy is "a system or organization in which people or groups are ranked one above the other according to status or authority."
- Anecdote and tradition represent the lowest quality of evidence. Anecdote refers to things like, "It worked for me", or "My friend got great gains from using this supplement," and tradition refers to things like, "Everyone does it this way" or "Bodybuilders have always trained like this." The reason anecdote and tradition are considered low-quality evidence is because there are too many unknown variables and things that aren't controlled.
- Next on the hierarchy is observational research, where scientists observe people in their free-living environments, collect some data on them, and then look for relationships between different variables.
- This type of research is higher quality than anecdote or tradition because the data has been systematically gathered from large numbers of people and formally analyzed. However, as mentioned earlier, it can only establish correlations (relationships), not cause and effect.
- Next, we have one of the highest quality forms of evidence: the randomized controlled trial, or RCT. In an RCT, scientists take a group of people and randomly divide them into two or more groups (hence the term

"randomized"). The scientists try to keep everything the same between the groups, except for one variable that they want to study, which is known as the independent variable. RCTs rank above observational research because their highly controlled nature allows them to establish cause and effect relationships.

• When a group of studies exists on a particular topic, a systematic review or meta-analysis can tell you where the weight of the evidence lies on that topic. This is why they occupy the top of the evidence pyramid. Systematic reviews and meta-analyses represent the highest level of evidence because they gather the best RCTs and research on a topic and show you what that research generally agrees on.

4

The Anatomy of Research

Our greatest weakness lies in giving up. The most certain way to succeed is always to try just one more time.

—THOMAS EDISON

NOW THAT YOU UNDERSTAND how science works and the hierarchy of evidence, it's time to learn how to read and understand scientific literature.

Becoming highly skilled at reading and interpreting scientific research requires many hours of graduate school training and studying the nuances of science and statistics, but the basics can be learned quickly and easily, which is what this section of the book will teach you.

Once you have the fundamentals under your belt, you'll be able to effectively evaluate many studies, understand their findings, and form your own conclusions about them.

Let's start with defining key terms.

Research Terminology

Before you learn to read research, it's important to understand the "language" of science—the terminology that scientists use when reporting on research.

Here are the main ones you'll see:

Population

All elements, individuals, or units that meet the selection criteria for a group to be studied.

Sample

A portion drawn from a population, the study of which is intended to lead to statistical estimates of the attributes of the whole population.

Prospective Study

A prospective study is one that starts in the present and continues forward in time. Scientists decide what they are going to do, start collecting data, and then analyze it at some point in the future. For example, RCTs are prospective studies.

Retrospective Study

A retrospective study is one that looks backward in time. Scientists collect data on things that have already happened, and then analyze it to look for important relationships and outcomes. Retrospective studies include some forms of observational research and can't establish cause and effect.

In Vitro Study

An in vitro (Latin for "in glass") study is one where scientists look at the effects of something outside its natural environment, as in a test tube or cell culture. For example, if you wanted to know how a supplement affects muscle cells, you could engineer muscle tissue that mimics the structure of real skeletal muscle and culture it with a supplement and see what happens. While in vitro research can be helpful in generating hypotheses and investigating physiological mechanisms, it can't replace research on animals or humans (known as in vivo [Latin for "in a living thing"] research).

Control Group

A control group is a group that receives no treatment or

some type of "usual" or "standard of care" treatment.

For example, a control group in a weight training study may do no training, a control group in a drug study may get an inert treatment (a sugar pill, for example), and a control group in a study looking at a particular physical therapy intervention may get the usual standard care.

Control groups are important because they help to reduce the impacts of things like psychological expectations and natural variation.

For instance, let's say you do a study comparing the effects of weight training to no training on blood pressure, and you find a small decrease in blood pressure in the weight training group. You also see one in the control group, though, which means that you can't claim the weight training caused a decrease in blood pressure because it happened in the "do-nothing" control group as well.

Placebo

A placebo is an inert or "does-nothing" substance or treatment given to subjects in a study. A placebo acts as a control in a study because it helps you eliminate the effects of psychological expectations on the results.

For example, let's say you're doing a study looking at the effects of a pre-workout supplement on muscle strength.

You give some subjects a placebo, which looks and tastes like the pre-workout supplement, but actually doesn't contain any active ingredients. At least some of the subjects will probably expect a pre-workout to enhance their strength, and these expectations alone can make them stronger regardless of what they drink. Therefore, if both the pre-workout and placebo groups show similar gains in strength, then you know that the effects of the pre-workout supplement were purely psychological. However, if the pre-workout group gained more strength than the placebo group, then you know that the pre-workout supplement can improve strength.

Double-Blind

In a double-blind study, neither the subjects nor the researchers know who's getting which treatment. This is done to help prevent either of their expectations from influencing the study outcomes.

For example, let's say you're going to study how protein supplementation compares to a placebo for gaining muscle and strength. In a double-blind study, the subjects and scientists wouldn't know whether they're getting or giving protein powder or the placebo until after all the data is analyzed.

Single-Blind

In a single-blind study, either the subjects *or* the researchers don't know what type of treatment the subjects received, but not both. This is a less stringent design than a double-blind study but is sometimes necessary because certain situations make it impossible to blind both the subjects and scientists.

For example, if a study compares real surgery to a "sham" one, you can hide the type of operation from the subject through general anesthesia and performing an incision instead of a full surgery, but it would be impossible to hide the type of surgery being performed from the surgeon.

Randomized

In a randomized study, subjects are randomly assigned to the various treatments. Randomization is important because it "levels the playing field" by reducing the likelihood that one group is significantly and meaningfully different from any other.

For example, let's say you have a study that tests how a fat-burning supplement and a placebo impact fat loss. Subjects are assigned to either the supplement group or the placebo group randomly. Sometimes one group can still be a little different from another, but not usually enough to impact the results.

Matched

In a study where subjects are matched, every person in a particular group is matched with an equivalent subject in another group. This helps ensure the groups are as similar as possible.

For example, let's say you have a study looking at the impact of caffeine on muscle strength. You separate subjects into a caffeine group and a placebo group, and for each subject of a given body weight and strength level you put in the caffeine group, you make sure a person of similar size and strength is put in the placebo group.

Crossover Design

In a crossover design, subjects receive more than one treatment during the study.

For example, let's say you want to examine the effects of an intra-workout supplement on fatigue while cycling. The subjects come to the gym and cycle while drinking the intra-workout supplement, and are tested to see how long they can maintain a given pace. One week later, they come to the gym again, take the placebo, and then are tested again on maintaining the pace.

Thus, rather than dividing the subjects into intra-workout and placebo groups, all of the people were subjected to both conditions. In many cases, this can be superior to a regular randomized controlled trial, because each subject acts as his own control (each gets both the placebo and intra-workout). This helps mitigate the effects of genetic variations among people that can greatly impact the results.

Washout Period

A washout period is a period of time between treatments to allow any residual effects of one treatment to disappear before you give another one.

Washout periods can be important in crossover studies because, without them, the effects of one treatment can "spill over" and impact the results of another treatment.

For example, let's say you're doing a crossover study on how taking creatine for 4 weeks affects muscle growth. You might have the subjects take creatine for 4 weeks, then have them go through an 8-week washout period where they stop taking creatine. Finally, you'd have the subjects take a placebo for 4 weeks.

Now, if you didn't have this 8-week washout period—if you went from 4 weeks of creatine supplementation directly into 4 weeks of placebo—the creatine levels in the subject's muscles would still be elevated from the supplementation. This would impact the results of the placebo treatment because it wouldn't be a true placebo.

Mean

The mean is the average value for a group. It's calculated by adding up all the numbers and then dividing the sum by how many numbers there are.

For example, if 5 people each gain 3, 5, 2, 6, and 4 pounds of muscle, this is what the math would look like:

$3 + 5 + 2 + 6 + 4 = 20$

$20 / 5 = 4$

So, the mean amount of muscle gain would be 4 pounds.

Standard Deviation (SD)

A standard deviation is a measure of how "spread out" the data is in a group, and specifically how spread out it is around the mean of the group. Thus, a high standard deviation means there's a lot of variation in the data (the values vary widely), and a low standard deviation means there isn't much variation (the values don't vary as much).

For example, the graph below represents data from a study that looked at the effects of drop sets on muscle and strength gains.[1] It shows the average percent change in 12-rep max performance in two groups, along with the standard deviation (the vertical bars).

You can see that the standard deviation was almost as large as the percentage change itself in the two groups, indicating that results varied widely from one person to the next in terms of strength gained.

AVERAGE % CHANGE IN TRICEPS PUSHDOWN 12-RM

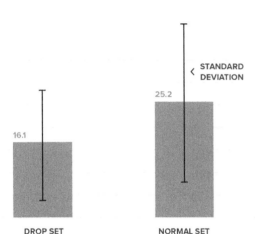

Standard Error

The standard error represents how closely the "true" average of an entire population was estimated.

Remember, when we perform studies, we can only look at samples of people, not entire populations. Then, we try to extrapolate what we find looking at that sample of people to the larger group we pulled them from. Standard error, then, gives us an idea of how accurate our estimates are because it's calculated in such a way that there's a 95% chance that the population average is within two standard errors of the mean.

The math used to calculate standard errors is fairly complicated so we won't get into it here, but let's see how it works by way of example.

Let's say I took a random sample of 100 men in the United States and measured their height, and let's say the average of that sample was 70 inches with a standard error of 2 inches. That would mean that my research would indicate that there's a 95% chance that the average height of all men in the U.S. is between 66 inches and 74 inches. (Remember, it's 2 standard errors, so give or take 4 inches in this case).

If I want to be more accurate (if I want a smaller standard error), then I need to increase my sample size. For example, if I tested 1,000 men instead, my standard error might decrease to 1.5 or 1. If I found the same thing, then I could say that there's a 95% chance that the average height of all men in the U.S. is between 68 inches and 72 inches.

Confidence Interval

A confidence interval is a range of values that contains a specified probability of the true (perfectly accurate) value of a given parameter.

That's a mouthful, so let's break it down.

As you know, in scientific studies, we can't study entire populations at once. Instead, we can take samples of people to study and then try to project our findings onto entire populations, and we use confidence intervals to indicate how certain we are that our projections are true.

Again, the math used to generate confidence intervals is beyond the scope of this book, but here's how it plays out:

Let's say you put people on a low-carb diet and they lose

an average of 5 pounds in 5 weeks. This doesn't mean that the entire population will necessarily achieve the same results, and we can calculate a confidence interval to estimate the range of values that would likely occur if the entire population followed the same diet.

Let's say that the confidence interval in this study is calculated to be 2 to 7 pounds with a probability of 95%. This would mean that if you repeated the same study with new samples of people from the same population, there's a 95% chance they would lose an average of anywhere from 2 to 7 pounds.

As you can see, the wider the confidence interval, the more uncertainty is involved in the estimation.

Effect Size

An effect size is a measurement used to represent the magnitude of an observed change.

Usually, it's the difference between two groups or time points in terms of standard deviations. An effect size of 1 means there was a change equal to one standard deviation.

Effect sizes are often classified as "trivial" (less than 0.2), "small" (0.2 to 0.49), "moderate" (0.5 to 0.79), or "large" (0.8 or more), although these classifications might vary depending upon what is being studied.

Cohort

A cohort is a group of subjects that's followed over time.

Cohort Study

A cohort study is a study where a single group (cohort) or multiple groups of subjects (cohorts) are followed over time, ranging from a number of days to many years.

Cross-Sectional Study

A cross-sectional study is similar to a cohort study, but instead of following groups over extended periods of time, you compare two different groups at a specific point in time.

The Anatomy of a Scientific Study

The vast majority of published studies have the following components:

- Abstract
- Introduction/Background
- Methods
- Statistical Analyses
- Results

- Discussion
- Conclusion
- Funding/Competing Interests

We'll review each.

As we go, I recommend you follow along with several full-text studies to get an idea of how all of this comes together. You can find four papers in the free bonus material that comes with this book (fitnesssciencebook.com/bonus), including twenty-six that James helped author.

All of these papers have the same sections we're about to go over, so pick one you like and start at the top, with the abstract.

Abstract

In this section, the researchers give you a quick summary of the study.

It gives a very brief description of what the researchers did, what their findings were, and usually a sentence or two showing the researcher's conclusions.

While the abstract can give you some important initial information about a paper, reading the abstract alone is not sufficient to evaluate the quality of a study and findings. A lot of important details regarding the quality of the design, execution, and results are often missing from the abstract. Also, sometimes the conclusions in the abstract aren't even supported by the data in the study, which is why you can't take them at face value.

Introduction/Background

In this section, researchers give you background information on the matter being investigated and why they did the study.

They will talk about relevant research that has been done in the past, what types of holes exist in the current knowledge, and often the purpose of their study and/or the hypothesis that the researchers tested. In other words, this part helps provide context and tells people why their study was worth doing.

Methods

In this section, researchers describe exactly what they did in the study.

They will discuss the design of the study, the subjects they recruited (or the types of animals used), the process they went through to collect data, the measurement tools they used, along with anything else important on how they performed the study.

Ideally, there is enough information in this section to allow other scientists to try to replicate it if they want.

Statistical Analyses

In this section, researchers describe the types of statistics they used to analyze the data.

Statistical analyses are important because they give us a good idea of whether the study's results are due to random chance or are thanks to the treatment (supplement, training plan, diet, etc.).

This section can be daunting to those who aren't well trained in statistics, but once you have a good understanding of the fundamentals (which you'll get later in this book), you can navigate them more easily.

Results

In this section, researchers describe the results of the study. It often contains tables, charts, and graphs of study outcomes.

Discussion

In this section, researchers discuss the results of the study and what they mean.

It often contains speculation on why they found what they did and may also describe the strengths and weaknesses of the study.

Conclusion

In this section, researchers will provide their overall conclusions on the results and may also share thoughts as to how they can be applied. Sometimes, the Conclusion is combined with the Discussion section.

Unfortunately, when reviewing research, many people gloss over the Methods and Discussion and go straight to the Conclusion. This can be problematic because by its very nature, the Conclusion is the *researcher's'* conclusions based on their own interpretation of their data.

They may have biases that impact those interpretations and judgments that you wouldn't be aware of unless you also reviewed the Methods, Results, and Discussion sections to form your own opinion of the data, which may or may not differ from that of the researchers.

A good example of how researchers can slant their conclusions is a study on the effects of whole grains on energy balance.[2] The scientists concluded that eating more calories from whole grains instead of refined grains could increase your metabolic rate. However, this isn't what happened in the study.

First, metabolic rate showed a slight decrease on the refined grain diet from baseline, and this may have been due to a small amount of weight loss or random chance. Furthermore, the researchers overstated how much whole grains might impact energy balance, claiming you could burn up to 92 more calories per day if you ate whole grains instead of refined grains. This was based on faulty calculations, however, and a more realistic number is around 57 additional calories per day.

Funding/Competing Interests

In the final section of a study, researchers will state who paid for the study and may also list any competing interests (anything that may interfere with an objective presentation of the research).

For example, if the study is on dairy and it was funded by one of the scientists who's on the board for the National Dairy Council, then this will be stated here.

If funding was provided by a company with a vested interest in the outcome (a supplement company funding research on its own products, for example), and/or the scientists themselves have competing interests, then you should regard the outcomes with a bit of skepticism.

For example, many of the early studies on HMB were done by Steve Nissen, its inventor and patent-holder. Some of these studies reported tremendously positive results that couldn't be replicated by other labs, which gives you a good reason to be skeptical of those early outcomes.

Another good example of industry bias is a systematic review in the British Medical Journal that found that research funded by drug companies was more likely to see a positive result than research that was not funded by drug companies.[3] There's also an important caveat, though: the overall quality of the industry-funded studies were as good as or better than the non-industry funded ones because they have more money to spend on research. Thus, it's possible that some of the difference in results is due to just that: better research.

This is one of the reasons you shouldn't immediately discount or dismiss a study based purely on funding sources. An industry funding a study doesn't also mean that industry agents are also involved in the data collection, analysis, and publication of results.

It's also worth noting that researchers can have their own conflicts of interest that have nothing to do with the source of funding, such as trying to renew grants, having their name on more publications, writing books or newspaper articles, or trying to attract customers to their products and services.

For example, Experimental and Applied Sciences (EAS) funded this study on glutamine supplementation, but the scientists were not employees of EAS nor affiliated with the company in any way.[4] EAS also had no role in the study or its publication, other than simply providing the money to do the research.

To give you an idea of how much study funding has a tendency to distort people's perceptions of a study's quality, there was a study done on 503 board-certified physicians and how the funding source influenced their opinions of the study's quality. The physicians believed that a study was of lower quality if it was corporate-sponsored, even when there was no actual methodological difference between the studies![5] This is why it's important to judge a study on its own merits rather than on the funding source.

Alan Aragon, a researcher in the field of nutrition, said it best:

"If you dismiss research based on funding source, you'd have to be consistent and dismiss all industry-sponsored research, and this includes research on meat, fish, eggs, nuts, vegetables, fruits, olive oil, grains, avocados, potatoes, you name it. You'd also have to dismiss all of the research funded by the Atkins Foundation and other low-carb interests. While you're at it, you would need to be consistent and dismiss all pharmaceutical research, and most supplement research for that matter. You can't just selectively dismiss research based on the funding source that you feel does not agree with your personal ideology."

You now understand the fundamentals of scientific research.

In fact, by just learning the meanings of key terminology, you now know more about the scientific method than most people ever will.

What's more, you also know enough to begin reading and evaluating studies. You'll understand what scientists did, what the results were, and how conclusions were formed. And more importantly, you'll know whether you agree with them and be able to articulate why.

That said, there's one element of scientific research that'll trip you up: statistics.

In many cases, the validity of an experiment hinges upon the collection and interpretation of statistical data, and as it's one of the more technically demanding aspects of science, it can seem impenetrable to the layman.

That's why we're going to tackle statistics in the next chapter.

Key Takeaways

- The vast majority of published studies have the following components: abstract, introduction/background, methods, statistical analyses, results, discussion, conclusion, funding/competing interests.
- The abstract describes what the researchers did, what their findings were, and usually a sentence or two showing the researcher's conclusions. A lot of important details regarding the quality of the design, execution, and results are often missing from the abstract, and reading the abstract alone is not sufficient to evaluate the quality of a study and findings.
- The introduction/background describes relevant research that has been done in the past, what types of holes exist in the current knowledge, and often the purpose of a study and/or the hypothesis that the researchers tested.
- The methods section describes the design of the study, the subjects they recruited (or the types of animals used), the process they went through to collect data, the measurement tools they used, along with anything else important on how they performed the study.
- The statistical analyses section describes the types of statistics the researchers used to analyze the data.
- The results section describes the findings of the study.
- The discussion section describes the results of the study and what they mean.
- The conclusion section describes the researcher's'

conclusions about the results and how they can be applied, based on their own interpretation of their data.

- The funding/competing interests section describes who paid for the study and may also list any competing interests (anything that may interfere with an objective presentation of the research). You shouldn't immediately discount or dismiss a study based purely on funding source, and researchers can have their own conflicts of interest that have nothing to do with the source of funding.

5

The Anatomy of Statistics

Mathematics is the language with which
God has written the universe.

—GALILEO GALILEI

STATISTICS INVOLVES COLLECTING and analyzing numerical data, and it plays a much more important role in scientific studies than many people realize.

A good or bad statistical analysis can be the difference between real or false findings, and there's an enormous amount of scientific research published with inadequate or inappropriate statistical methods.

Since most people—including most journalists—don't have a strong background in statistics, it's impossible for them to review studies and recognize bad statistics when they exist, which is one of the reasons why so many false ideas are still circulating in the mainstream.

In this section, you'll learn the basics of the types of statistics used in studies so you can better understand how data is manipulated to produce findings, and better recognize common mistakes and problems that occur.

Statistical Inference

The primary purpose of statistics is to make some type of inference (logical conclusion based on evidence) about a population, based on a sample from that population.

For example, let's say you have a classroom of people and want to know their average body weight. How might you go about it? The easiest way, of course, is to weigh everyone and calculate the average. What if you can't do that, though? What if there are 200 people in your classroom? How might you calculate the average weight? This is more difficult, but it can be done through the use of statistics.

What you can do is choose 50 people from the room at random, calculate their average weight, and infer that the average weight of the entire room is probably similar. This won't be perfect, of course, but it'll be more right than wrong.

How can you increase the accuracy of that inference? Well, you can increase the sample size to, let's say, 100 people, and recalculate. That'll bring you closer to the true average, and as you continue to increase your sample size, you'll get even closer.

The two key points here are:

Analyzing samples from a larger group will give you a

reasonable estimate of whatever you're measuring, but there will always be a certain amount of error.

1. The larger your sample size, the more accurate your estimates become (the amount of error decreases). The smaller your sample size, the less accurate your estimates become (the amount of error increases).
2. This is why you need to pay attention to variables such as sample size and error when looking at the statistics of a study. If your sample size is too small and/or your error is too large, the conclusions of the paper can be questionable.

Estimating Error

When scientists refer to *error*, they're referring to a measurement of the estimated difference between what they've observed or calculated and the true values.

In other words, it's a numerical representation of how likely the researcher's data and/or interpretations are to be correct, and there are a few ways the amount of error can be expressed:

1. Standard Error
2. Confidence Interval
3. Standard Deviation

We discussed these earlier in the book, but for the sake of clarity, here's how they could look in our classroom example above:

- Mean height of sample: 68 inches
- Number of people in sample: 50 people (out of a classroom of 200)
- Standard error of sample: 0.70 inches. We recall that this means that there's a 95% chance that the average height of the entire class is within twice this amount of the mean.
- Confidence interval: The 95% interval is 68 ± 1.4, or 66.6 to 69.4 inches. This means there's a 95% chance that the average height of the entire 200-person classroom is between 66.6 and 69.4 inches.
- Standard deviation of sample: 5 inches. This means that about 68 percent of the people in the sample fall within "68 ± 5," or the range of 63 to 72 inches.

Comparing Groups

As you know, many research studies involve comparing two or more groups of people or animals, and various types of statistical analyses can help us determine whether the differences we see are true differences or just due to random chance.

For example, let's say that we now have two classrooms, each with 300 people and want to know if the average weight of one is different from the other. Again, we can't just weigh everyone, but we can take a sample of people from each room, calculate their average weights, and then use statistics to help us compare and interpret these numbers.

Here's how this might play out: Let's say we take 50 people

from each room and the average weight for the first sample is 150 pounds, and the average weight for second is 160 pounds. Does this mean that the average weight of the first classroom is indeed lower than the second? Not so fast. The differences in our samples could just be due to random chance or natural variation, not because the averages are actually different.

To get a better idea as to whether our samples represent a true difference, we'd run a *statistical test* to determine the probability that our findings do indeed reflect reality. There are many types of statistical tests, and some of the more common and basic ones include t-tests, analysis of variance (ANOVA), and Wilcoxon tests.

- A t-test is usually used when we want to compare two groups.
- An ANOVA is usually used when we want to compare three or more groups.
- A Wilcoxon test is similar to a t-test, but is used when our data doesn't follow a normal "bell curve" distribution (more on this later).

When we run one of these statistical tests, we get what's called a *test statistic*—a number that indicates how likely our observation or calculation is to be true.

For example, let's say we do a t-test to compare the two averages in our classroom analysis, and it's calculated to be a 2. This is our test statistic, and from it, we'll use a mathematical formula to generate what's called a *p-value*, which represents the probability that we'd observe a test statistic of this magnitude or greater if there was actually no difference in average weight between the groups (if our findings were just due to chance).

So, let's say the p-value is calculated to be 0.15. This means there's a 15 percent chance that we'd calculate a test statistic of 2 or more from the data if our findings weren't true.

Technically speaking, this simplification isn't *entirely* correct, but it serves our purposes here just fine.

Now, when a p-value is 0.05 or less, we call the results *statistically significant,* and this is the cutoff level used in the vast majority of research. If a p-value is higher than 0.05, then any observed differences are rejected as too uncertain.

Why 0.05, you ask?

There's nothing magical about this level—it's an arbitrary agreement among scientists as to what level of uncertainty is acceptable.

What this means, then, is that p-values higher than 0.05 don't automatically mean that research is "wrong" or "worthless." A result that gives a p-value of 0.07 may still represent a meaningful effect, even if it can't be said to be statistically significant.

For example, in a meta-analysis looking at the effects of the number of resistance training sets on muscle size, fewer than 9 weekly sets showed a 5.8 percent increase in muscle size, while 9 or more weekly sets showed an 8.2 percent increase.[6] The p-value for this difference was 0.076, so while not "statistically significant," it was close, and 8.2 versus 5.8 percent can be a meaningful difference if you want to maximize muscle growth. Therefore, it would be reasonable to recommend that you do more than 9 sets per week for whatever muscle groups you want to grow the most.

Likewise, just because a result is statistically significant doesn't mean it's meaningful. For example, let's say you find a resistance training study that compared a 3-set program to a 5-set program. The 5-set program showed a greater increase in bench press by 3 pounds with a p-value of 0.05. This finding is statistically significant and could be used to create splashy headlines ("Want a Bigger Bench, Bro? Do 5 Sets, Not 3"), but is 3 pounds all that meaningful?

Not really.

Type I and II Errors

If a statistically significant result is achieved in a study when, in reality, there's no difference, this is a type I error. In other words, a type I error is a false positive result.

Let's go back to our example above of calculating the average weights of two classrooms of 300 people. Let's say that the average weight for my sample from one of the rooms is 170 pounds and the average from the other is 155 pounds, and my statistical test finds the difference to be statistically significant. I can then state that my analysis demonstrates the people in the first room are, on average, heavier than those in the second.

However, let's say the true average weights of the rooms are the same—165 pounds. In this case, I have a false positive or a type I error because I have declared a difference when there really is none.

This can happen based on pure random chance. For example, let's say I take a very small sample of only 4 people per group. With such a small sample size, there's a chance I end up with a few tall people in one group, and a few short people in the other, producing a "statistically significant" result that was, in fact, just luck.

As you've probably guessed, a type II error is the opposite: a false negative. Sticking with the same example, let's say I take a sample of just 10 people from each classroom and find the average weight to be 150 pounds for one and 155 pounds for the other.

I run my statistical test and the difference isn't statistically significant, meaning there's a high probability that the difference is due to random chance or natural variation. Therefore, I state that my analysis doesn't support the claim that the people in the second room are, on average, heavier than those in the first.

However, let's say the true average weight of the first room is 152 pounds, and the true average weight of the second is 160 pounds. In this case, my finding was actually accurate, but I have a type II error. Similar to type I errors, one of the main reasons this can happen is small sample sizes, which makes it harder to detect statistically meaningful differences.

A prime example of a type II error is the early research on a weightlifting method known as High Intensity Training (HIT). Several studies found that people who did 1 set or multiple sets gained the same amount of strength.[7]

Many HIT gurus used this as proof that you don't need to do more than 1 set.

However, the sample sizes in these studies were too small to adequately detect a difference between groups. More recent studies have shown that multiple sets produce better strength gains than 1 set, which means the earlier results were false negatives or type II errors.[8]

The Multiple Comparison Problem

Studies that involve the comparison of multiple groups are particularly prone to type I errors.

Let's say I'm conducting a study that involves comparing effects in 4 groups: A, B, C, and D. That means I need to make 6 comparisons—A to B, A to C, A to D, B to C, B to D, C to D—and the more comparisons that are involved in a study, the more likely I am to see a false positive result (the more likely random chance can produce what appears to be a positive result).

To understand why, let's illustrate this further. Say you have a 1 in 20 (5%) chance of a false positive for each of the six comparisons that you're going to do, which are reasonable odds. It stands to reason, then, that more comparisons means there's a higher likelihood you'll get at least one false positive result.

To calculate this precisely, you don't simply multiply the individual likelihood (5%) by the number of comparisons (6), but instead, you take the chance of NOT producing a false positive result (95%) to the power of the number of comparisons done (6), and then subtract from one.

Essentially what you're doing here is first determining your overall chance of producing an accurate result, which of course then tells you how likely an inaccurate result is. Here's how the math looks:

1 - 0.95^6 = 0.26 or 26%

This means you have about a 1 in 4 chance of seeing a false positive if you do 6 comparisons. If you were to do 10 comparisons, the math looks like this:

1 - 0.95^{10} = 0.40 or 40%

This means, with 10 comparisons, you can expect at least one false positive result 40% of the time.

The solution is to make statistical adjustments that allow for more accurate analysis of multiple comparisons. Names for these statistical adjustments include Tukey, Bonferonni, Holm, Sidak, and Hochberg corrections, and if you're reading a study that involves multiple comparisons and you don't see one of these corrections, then you should be wary of positive results.

Unfortunately, many researchers don't adjust for multiple comparisons when they should. This is likely because, surprisingly, many don't learn about the statistical challenges of multiple comparisons, or simply fail to recognize when adjustments for multiple comparisons are necessary.

It's Important to Be Normal

Many statistical tests are based on what are called *parametric statistics*, which assumes that your data follows a *normal distribution*, or *bell curve*, that you can compare your findings against.

A normal distribution is an arrangement of data in which most values cluster in the middle, and the rest taper off toward the ends, like this:

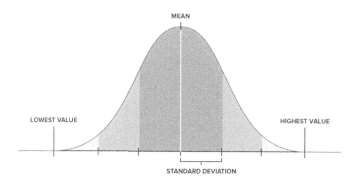

As you can see, it's called a "bell curve" due to its shape, and the middle represents the average value for the data and as you move away, values are increasingly above or below the average.

Many things closely follow this type of distribution, including the heights and blood pressure levels of large groups of people, the size of specific things produced by machines, and grades in testing. In other words, most people will be a similar height and have similar blood pressure levels, most things produced by machines will be similar in size, and most people will get similar grades.

Many things don't follow this type of distribution, though, such as annual household income in the U.S., neighborhood housing prices, and retirement age, which look like this:

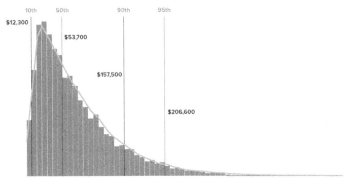

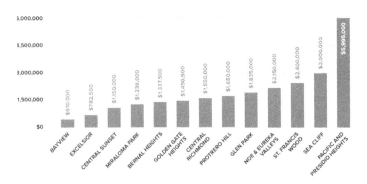

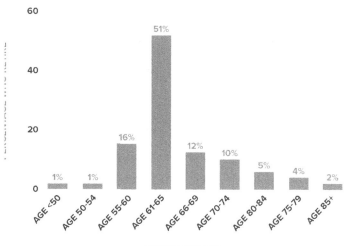

AVERAGE AMERICAN RETIREMENT AGE

It's important for researchers to test whether their data fits a normal distribution or not with tests like the Shapiro-Wilk, Anderson-Darling, and Kolmogorov-Smirnov. If the data doesn't fit a normal distribution, then the researchers either need to apply special calculations to *transform* it to fit, or use a *non-parametric* statistical test, which doesn't assume your data is normally distributed. Examples of non-parametric tests include Wilcoxon, Mann-Whitney, Friedman, or Kruskal-Wallis tests.

Unfortunately, many researchers don't check to see if their data fits the statistical tests that they use, and this can lead to invalid results. This is because many statistical tests are based on assumptions about the data being analyzed, and if the assumptions don't hold true, then the test results might not be accurate.

Examples of Good and Not-So-Good Statistics in Research

To see all of this in action, let's analyze the statistics of two actual studies.

As you'll see, one has severe limitations in the statistical methods, which likely skewed the outcomes, and the other has solid statistical procedures.

The Not-So-Good Study

Bocarsly, M. E., Powell, E. S., Avena, N. M., & Hoebel, B. G. (2010). High-fructose corn syrup causes characteristics of obesity in rats: increased body weight, body fat and triglyceride levels. Pharmacology Biochemistry and Behavior, 97(1), 101-106.

In this study, researchers found that rats who ate more calories from fructose gained more body fat than those who ate more sucrose (table sugar). At least that's what they reported.

As you'll see, there were numerous problems with the study, particularly in the statistical methodology. The statistical methods section reads as follows:

"Data from all groups were compared using ANOVAs, or repeated measures ANOVA, when appropriate, followed by post hoc pair-wise comparisons, when justified."

Yup, that's it. The statistical methods section was *one sentence*. This is a bright red flag for the reader because it gives the impression that little thought was put into the statistical analyses in this study. We can't be certain that's the case, of course, but even if the methodology was much more detailed than described, they don't give us much to work with.

First, remember that most statistical tests are based on parametric statistics that assume your data follows a "bell curve." Analysis of Variance (ANOVA), which was used in this study, is a parametric statistical procedure. However, the researchers make no mention of whether they tested if their data fit into a bell curve, and if it didn't, then an ANOVA isn't the right test. In that case, you'd either have to transform the data and *then* run the ANOVA, or use a non-parametric test, like a Kruskal-Wallis test.

Second, there's the problem of multiple comparisons. Remember that you have to adjust your statistics when you're comparing more than two groups because if you don't, there's a greater chance of producing false positives (type I errors).

In this study, up to 4 groups of rats were compared to each other, and there's no mention of any statistical adjustments for multiple comparisons. They simply stated they did "*post hoc comparisons*," which simply means comparisons done after their initial test.

They basically said, "We did some stuff to the numbers after the fact, but don't worry about it."

Not very helpful.

They don't tell us whether they ever adjusted for the fact that they were comparing multiple groups. If they didn't—and we have no reason to believe they did—then there's a much higher chance the results were a false positive.

Sure enough, there's reason to believe that's the case. When you look at the data, you can see that the results were all over the place, with some rats gaining more or less body fat across all of the experiments. In other words, some of the rats eating lots of fructose didn't gain much body fat, and some of the rats eating lots of sugar did.

Scattershot results like that make the chances of a false positive even higher.

The problems don't end there, though.

The researchers also didn't report any confidence intervals for their results, so we don't know how much uncertainty there was in the results. For example, if all of the groups had wide confidence intervals, and those confidence intervals overlapped significantly, then we couldn't be very confident that there's any real difference between the groups.

Since they didn't include these, we'll never know.

Finally, the researchers also didn't give us precise p-values. Instead, researchers reported them as "P > 0.05" if the results weren't statistically significant. This is important because "P > 0.05" could mean 0.06 or 0.26, and as a reader, you'd want to know this because while a p-value of 0.06 doesn't meet the arbitrary criterion for statistical significance (0.05), it can still represent a meaningful result worth noting.

The bottom line is that the researchers didn't give us enough information to know how likely their results are to be true. If the authors of a paper don't include what statistical tests they ran, then it's fair to assume that they didn't run them.

And that means the results just aren't as valuable.

The Better Study

Martins, C., Truby, H., & Morgan, L. M. (2007). Short-term appetite control in response to a 6-week exercise programme in sedentary volunteers. British Journal of Nutrition, 98(4), 834-842.

In this study, researchers looked at the effects of a 6 week exercise program on appetite, and based on what was reported in the paper, its statistical methods are much stronger than the previous study.

To start, the statistical methods section is five paragraphs long. Many papers dedicate just a paragraph to statistics (or even a sentence, as we saw above), so the fact that these scientists placed this much emphasis on their statistics is a good sign.

The researchers also checked to see if their data is normally distributed:

"All variables were checked regarding their normal distribution using the Shapiro-Wilk test."

Next, they described every type of comparison performed and the tests used, which were properly chosen.

The study involved multiple comparisons, and they explained how they adjusted for it:

"In order to correct for multiple comparisons, the level of significance (α level) was reduced to $P < 0.01$."

In the Results section, the researchers reported the precise p-values, even for non-significant results. For example, when comparing the baseline calorie intake between two groups, they report the p-value as 0.925 rather than simply saying P > 0.05. This helps you know whether a certain result may have been close to statistical significance (in this particular example, it wasn't even close).

About the only thing missing from this study are confidence intervals. Despite that one limitation, this study is far more robust than many others in its statistical methods.

Faulty statistics can scuttle even the most beautifully designed and executed study, so it's vitally important to understand how the common statistical methods and tools work.

This way, you can know how much stock to put in research and how likely the outcomes are as they appear.

Furthermore, when researchers engage in shenanigans, it often involves perverting statistical data to support their biases or preexisting conclusions. This works with people who are statistically illiterate, but is less likely to escape notice from someone who has read this chapter.

In the next chapter, we're going to distill everything we've covered so far into a practical checklist you can use when reading and evaluating research.

Key Takeaways

- Statistics involves collecting and analyzing numerical data, and a good or bad statistical analysis can be the difference between real or false findings, and there's an enormous amount of scientific research published with inadequate or inappropriate statistical methods.
- The primary purpose of statistics is to make some type of inference (logical conclusion based on evidence) about a population, based on a sample from that population.
- When scientists refer to error, they're referring to a measurement of the estimated difference between what they've observed or calculated and the true values. In other words, it's a numerical representation of how likely the researcher's data and/or interpretations are to be correct.
- Many research studies involve comparing two or more groups of people or animals, and various types of statistical analyses can help us determine whether the differences we see are true differences or just due to random chance.
- When a statistically significant result is achieved in a study when, in reality, there's no difference, this is a type I error. In other words, a type I error is a false positive result. A type II error is the opposite: a false negative.
- Studies that involve the comparison of multiple groups are particularly prone to type I errors.

- Many statistical tests are based on what are called parametric statistics, which assumes that your data follows a normal distribution, or bell curve, that you can compare your findings against. Many things don't follow this type of distribution, though, and this can change the results. Unfortunately, many researchers don't check to see if their data fits the statistical tests that they use, and this can lead to invalid results.

6

How to Rapidly Evaluate Research

Nothing in life is to be feared, it is only to be understood.

—MARIE CURIE

THE FOLLOWING CHECKLIST can be used as a guide for evaluating the quality of a study.

While it doesn't include *everything* you should look for when fully evaluating a study (because that would be beyond the scope of this book), it's a helpful cheat sheet for identifying characteristics that indicate higher or lower quality research.

You can also find this checklist as a PDF in the free bonus material that comes with this book (fitnesssciencebook.com/bonus).

Is it an in vitro (test tube) study, an animal study, or a human study?

In vitro studies can only help identify mechanisms or generate hypotheses, but they can't tell you much about what'll happen in real-life situations.

For example, if I culture muscle cells with creatine, it might give me an idea as to how creatine helps muscle cells grow, but it can't tell me what happens when people actually eat creatine because the circumstances are very different (test tube versus human body).

Animal studies are usually very well controlled, but the results may not be applicable to humans, because animal physiology, while similar to humans, isn't the same. For example, rodents have a much greater capacity to convert carbs to fat than humans, which means that high- versus low-carb studies in rodents are not necessarily applicable to people.

Human studies have the best real-life application, but sometimes aren't as well controlled as animal research. Therefore, it's important to not take human research at face value and to come to your own conclusions by analyzing its various components.

Is the study observational, a controlled trial, or a systematic review/meta-analysis?

An observational study can show relationships and help generate hypotheses, but it can't establish cause and effect, whereas a controlled trial can establish cause and effect, and a systematic review/meta-analysis can give you an idea of the weight of the evidence.

If it's an observational study, is it retrospective or prospective?

A prospective design is usually superior to a retrospective design because it can reduce bias by establishing baseline characteristics before the study starts.

In other words, it's better to come up with some hypotheses, take measurements, then see how things play out over time than to look at what happened in the past.

If it's an observational study, is it a cross-sectional or cohort study?

A cohort study is usually superior because you follow the same subjects over time, rather than comparing one group of subjects to another group in a given moment in time, even if those groups are similar.

If it's a controlled trial, were subjects randomized to their respective groups?

Randomizing subjects is superior because it ensures that groups are similar and start off on a level playing field.

If it's a randomized controlled trial, are the different groups independent, or is it a crossover design (where subjects receive more than one treatment)?

A cross-over design is usually superior because each subject acts as his/her own control, which can reduce genetic variability.

Were subjects and/or researchers blinded to the treatments?

It's best if both the subjects and scientists are blinded ("double-blind"), but one being blinded is better than none.

How long did the study last for?

Studies can last for hours, days, weeks, or years.

Short-term studies that look at the immediate effects of something (like the impact of a particular exercise on post-exercise fatigue over several hours) are known as acute studies. These are usually more highly controlled and can give you insights into mechanisms, but the results can't always be extrapolated to the long term.

Chronic studies that last weeks, months, or even years can give you a better idea of what happens over the long term, but usually such studies are not as highly controlled.

So, there's a tradeoff between how long a study lasts and how relevant the results are to the real world (where everything is long-term). Keep in mind, however, that just because a study is short doesn't necessarily mean it's bad. What matters is that the length of the study is enough to accurately answer the question at hand.

Furthermore, you should know that short-term results in studies on diet, training, and supplementation often don't extrapolate cleanly into long-term ones. For example, studies show that people who are new to weightlifting can gain several pounds of muscle per month at first, but this quickly diminishes as time goes on.

What type of subjects were used?

Were the subjects young? Old? Obese? Normal weight? Women? Men? Rats?

The type of subjects used can matter because the results may not necessarily be applicable to other populations.

For example, young people gain more muscle in response to the same resistance training program as compared to older individuals, so if a study comes out showing that a particular training program caused a 5 lb muscle gain in three months in a group of twenty-something guys, that doesn't mean it's going to do the same for middle-aged or elderly people.[1]

Is the description of the methods and statistics detailed enough to where you could confidently replicate the study if you wanted to?

As you read through the methods, you should get an idea of whether you could replicate the study based on how much detail is offered, even if you don't quite understand everything presented. Basically, the more detail there is on the methods, the better.

For example, a study might say that "resting metabolic rate was tested." Does that tell you enough to replicate the study in the same fashion? No.

What you'd want to see is something like, "Resting metabolic rate was tested between 6 and 8 AM after an overnight fast. Subjects were instructed to refrain from any exercise, caffeine, or alcohol for at least 24 hours prior to the test. Resting metabolic rate was tested using indirect calorimetry via a metabolic cart and ventilated hood, and measurements were taken with subjects lying quietly supine, but awake. Measurements were taken continuously for at least 20 minutes to ensure steady state."

Did the researchers perform all their measurements under standardized conditions?

When scientists perform measurements, it's important that the conditions under which those measurements are taken are controlled (supervised to ensure all influencing factors are taken into account), and kept the same for each subject over time.

For example, if the scientists are measuring body composition, they should make sure the subjects are tested in the morning, after an overnight fast, and wearing the same clothing at the beginning and the end of the study.

Is the description of the results, along with the tables and graphs, sufficient enough to allow you to come to your own conclusions regarding the data?

Similar to the description of a study's methods, the more detail given on the results, the better.

For example, if the researchers only present some averages, standard deviations or standard errors, and p-values, that isn't enough information to evaluate the underlying data those calculations were based on.

On the other hand, if they also include things like confidence intervals, scatter plots of individual results, and effect sizes (which are a measure of the meaningfulness of an effect), that allows you to do a much deeper analysis of the results and determine if you agree with their conclusions.

Here are some more follow-up questions to ask yourself about how the data was presented.

Do the researchers present the data in just one way (such as the average before and after), or in multiple ways (like the average before/after, the absolute and percent change in each group, and the confidence interval for that change)?

Do the researchers just put the results in graph format (where it can be tough to discern exact numbers visually), or do they present the data both in text format and graph format?

Do the researchers present the data on different subgroups of people? For example, if not all subjects finished the study, do the researchers present results for everyone (also called an intent-to-treat analysis) as well as the results of the people who completed the study?

This is important because it can give you information as to how drop-outs may have affected the results. For example, let's say most of the drop-outs in a diet study were women, and most of the people who finished were men. This would imply that the diet being studied might be tougher for women to stick to.

What is the sample size of the study?

The smaller the sample size is, the more trouble you have detecting small effects because there can be more variation between people than the size of the change you're looking for.

For example, let's say you want to conduct a study to see if a high-volume weight training program can cause a larger increase in muscle size than a low-volume program, and your sample size is small (just 10 participants). We already know that people tend to respond very differently to resistance training, so a few of the subjects might gain a large amount of muscle while a few might gain almost none, and with only 10 participants, the data can come in all over the place. This, in turn, will make it difficult to reliably determine whether any differences that you might observe between the programs are true.

Another problem with a small sample size is that you may be more likely to show larger-than-normal effects due to outliers having more influence on outcomes.

Therefore, studies with larger sample sizes carry more weight than studies with small sample sizes. What constitutes a "small" sample size depends upon the question being asked, but typically, anything less than 10 to 20 subjects per group is considered a small sample size.

If the sample size is small, did the researchers present individual results?

When there's a small number of subjects, it can be helpful to see a scatterplot of how each individual person responded, to determine how it varied between people and whether there were outliers.

Are the reported results consistent between the abstract, results section, and discussion section?

Review what's written in the Abstract, Results, and Discussion sections, and if they don't all agree, that's a red flag.

Do the results make sense? Does something seem "off" about the results, or are the results wildly inconsistent with other studies in the area?

How this might play out can vary widely from one study to the next, and even true results can sometimes seem counter-intuitive or "off." However, if something is strikingly unusual or at odds with the weight of the evidence on the matter, it can be a red flag (highlighting the importance of replication in the scientific process).

For example, one lab has produced extremely positive muscle-building results with the supplement HMB—results that are better than what you see with anabolic steroids—but other labs have been unable to reproduce such amazing results.[2,3]

If the results are statistically significant, are they meaningful?

A statistically significant result isn't necessarily a meaningful one.

For example, if you saw a 25% increase in strength in one group and a 27% increase in another group, and the difference was statistically significant, how meaningful is it? Unless you're a strength athlete, it's not.

Another example can be seen in weight loss studies. For example, let's say a study shows that a low-carb group lost an average of 2 more pounds than a high-carb group over 6 months. That's not a meaningful difference over that time period and so it would be disingenuous to claim that low-carb dieting is simply "better" for weight loss.

Did the researchers report exact p-values for the results?

Exact p-values are better than vague statements like "$P > 0.05$" or "$P < 0.05$" because they give you a better idea as to the overall strength of the results.

Remember that just because an effect doesn't reach the level of statistical significance doesn't mean it should be dismissed out of hand.

Did the researchers present confidence intervals for the results?

Confidence intervals give you information regarding the precision or certainty of the data (the wider the confidence interval, the more uncertainty in the data).

Simple means and standard deviations can't give you this information, so the inclusion of confidence intervals is very helpful for evaluating the results of the study.

Did the researchers thoroughly discuss the limitations of their study?

If researchers don't discuss the limitations of their studies (and all studies have them), you, the reader, have no idea how they might have impacted results, how the study results might apply to the real world, and what questions the study can and can't answer.

If it's a diet study, was food intake well controlled (provided in a ward setting, for example), or was it self-reported?

Remember that self-report of food intake can be highly inaccurate, so the more control there is over food intake, the better.

If it's an exercise study, was the exercise supervised?

Similar to food intake, self-report of exercise (what was and wasn't done in workouts) can be unreliable, so the more control and supervision there is over the exercise program, the better.

Who funded the study? Did the researchers report any conflicts of interest?

While funding sources don't automatically invalidate studies, they can give good reason to be more skeptical of the results. The same goes for a conflict of interest—you shouldn't dismiss research based solely on this factor, but it should be taken into account when evaluating a study.

Putting It All Together: Evaluating Two Studies

Now that you've learned how to understand and evaluate some of the fundamentals of scientific research, let's see how to use what you know to evaluate two studies.

Study #1
Low-Carb vs. High-Carb For Fat Loss

Hall, K. D., Bemis, T., Brychta, R., Chen, K. Y., Courville, A., Crayner, E. J., ... & Miller, B. V. (2015). Calorie for calorie, dietary fat restriction results in more body fat loss than carbohydrate restriction in people with obesity. Cell metabolism, 22(3), 427-436.

This study compared the effects of a low-carb, high-fat diet to a high-carb, low-fat diet on body fat loss.

It had all the hallmarks of well-designed and well-executed research:

- **Randomized cohort trial**. Subjects were randomly assigned to either a low-carbohydrate or high-carbohydrate group, who were then followed over time. This allowed the study to establish cause and effect.
- **Crossover design**. After 5 days of a baseline diet (where all of the subjects ate the same foods, to make sure they all started on a "level playing field" so to speak) and 6 days of either the low-carb or high-carb diet, there was a 2 to 4 week washout period, which is long enough to ensure the effects of one diet didn't carry over to the next. Then, subjects who got low-carb the first time around got the high-carb diet, and vice versa, which is ideal because it allowed the scientists to compare the subjects to themselves.
- **Metabolic ward**. Subjects were housed in a metabolic ward during the study, which is a hospital ward designed to allow researchers to precisely control the subject's food intake and physical activity levels and do precise measurements of energy expenditure, carb burning, and fat burning.

- **Diets were protein and calorie matched**. Subjects consumed the same amount of protein and calories, which meant that any changes in body fat levels were due to the carb/fat ratio, not differences in calorie or protein intake.
- **Detailed methodology**. The methods of the study were thoroughly described, which would allow an independent scientist to replicate the experiment if desired.
- **Detailed statistical analysis**. A detailed description of the statistics were provided, which would allow an independent scientist to replicate the statistical analysis as well. The description included the software and procedures used, as well as calculations to determine how many subjects would be needed for the study.
- **Detailed tables and diagrams for all outcomes**. This allows you to thoroughly evaluate the outcomes, as opposed to having to rely on the researcher's interpretations of the data.
- **Actual p-values reported in the results**. Rather than stating things like "$P > 0.05$" or "$P = NS$" for nonsignificant results, researchers reported the actual p-values, so you can make your own assessment of the strength of the data.
- **Comparison results with a computer model of body composition change**. Dr. Kevin Hall has developed sophisticated computer models that predict body composition change in response to different diets. The results of this study were compared to the predictions made by the computer models, and were found to

match up fairly well. When real world results match results of a well-tested computer simulation, this can give you more confidence in both the observed results and the reliability of the computer model.

- **Analysis of body composition changes using multiple techniques (metabolic measurements and DEXA)**. Simultaneous measurement of body composition changes by different techniques reinforces the results if the changes are similar.

- **Extensive evaluation of study limitations in the Discussion section**. This is important because it helps you understand how the study results can be applied to the real world, and demonstrates what questions it can and can't answer.

- **Independent funding**. The study was funded by the National Institutes of Health, and there were no conflicts of interest among any of the researchers.

Study #2
BCAA vs. Carbohydrate Supplementation on Body Composition

Dudgeon, W. D., Kelley, E. P., & Scheett, T. P. (2016). In a single-blind, matched group design: branched-chain amino acid supplementation and resistance training maintains lean body mass during a caloric restricted diet. Journal of the International Society of Sports Nutrition, 13(1), 1.

This study compared the effects of BCAA supplementation

to carbohydrate supplementation on body composition in resis-
tance-training men on a calorie-restricted diet.

It had numerous flaws, some of which were pointed out in
a letter to the editor by other scientists.[4] These flaws include:

- **Lack of supervision of the resistance training
  program**. The subjects simply self-reported their training with training logs. Thus, there's no way to know if
  both groups used the same volume or intensity.
- **Single blind**. It was not clear from the study whether
  the subjects or the researchers were blinded to the
  treatments. Either way, it opens the door for bias to
  sneak into the results.
- **Poor dietary control**. The subjects were told to
  follow calorie-restricted diets, but they were allowed
  to prepare all of their own meals and weren't even
  required to write down what they ate. The researchers
  only verified their food intake by interviewing them
  after the fact. (facepalm)
- **Lack of detail in methodology**. Important details are
  missing from the methods section. For example, what
  type of resistance training program did the subjects
  do? This is important to know because different training programs can have different effects on lean body
  mass, which could confound the results (you want all
  the subjects doing the same program in a study like
  this). Were body composition and resting metabolic
  rate measured after an overnight fast? This too is
  important to know because, if you're not fasted during

these measurements, it can affect their accuracy. Were the BCAA and carbohydrate supplements similar in appearance and flavor? This matters because, if they weren't, then subjects might have been able to guess whether they got BCAAs or carbs, which can change behavior and expectations and affect the results.

- **Poor standardization of measurements**. When you perform measurements on subjects before and after a study, every aspect of the measurement should be done in the exact same way. This is especially important for measurements like body composition and resting metabolic rate, which can be impacted by time of day and when and what you last ate. The researchers said they tried to do measurements at the same time each day, but didn't give any other details.

- **Inappropriate statistics**. The researchers didn't check if their data met important assumptions like normality (the "bell curve"). They also used several t-tests to analyze their data, which was not appropriate for their experimental design because it involved multiple comparisons, and they didn't adjust for that.

- **Inconsistencies in reported data**. The results reported in the Abstract and Results sections don't agree with the results in the data. Specifically, in the abstract, the researchers stated that the BCAA group lost 0.05 kg, but this was not reported anywhere in the paper. Also, the reported standard errors in the graphs don't match with the values reported in the text, which in turn don't match the reported values in the abstract.

In other words, the reported results are all over the place.

- **Weird, inexplicable results**. Typically, when someone loses weight, their resting metabolic rate decreases due to a loss of lean body mass. In this case, resting metabolic rate dropped in the BCAA group but not in the carbohydrate group despite lean mass reportedly decreasing in the carbohydrate group but not the BCAA group. In other words, the subjects that drank BCAAs apparently preserved lean mass that the subjects drinking carbs didn't, but the metabolic data suggests the opposite.

- **Small sample size**. There were only 8 subjects in each group and the researchers failed to report their individual results. This can be important in small studies because it allows you to see how much the results differed between people.

- **No discussion of study limitations in the Discussion section**. This isn't good because you have no idea how the limitations (and *all* studies have them) might have impacted the results, how the study results might apply to the real world, and what questions the study can or can't answer.

- **Funding source was a supplement company that sells a BCAA supplement**. Despite this, the researchers reported no conflicts of interest. While this alone doesn't invalidate the study, it does give yet another reason to look at the research askance.

7

The Complete Beginner's Guide to Scientific Journals

*Most people say that it is the intellect which makes a
great scientist. They are wrong: it is character.*

—ALBERT EINSTEIN

YOU NOW KNOW MORE than most people ever will about
the ins and outs of scientific research, and you're well equipped
to venture into the literature and evaluate studies.

To do that, though, you need to know how to find studies, and that requires learning about where they're published:
scientific journals.

What Are Scientific Journals?

Scientific journals are generally monthly publications that compile studies related to a particular topic. You can find journals on just about any topic in science, and in the area of fitness in particular, there are dozens of journals that specialize in exercise and nutrition science. You can also find these types of studies in general physiology and metabolism journals.

For a study to get published in a scientific journal, it must go through a process called *peer review*. As you may remember from earlier in the book, peer review involves independent scientists (typically 2 to 3) reviewing the study for flaws before it's published. After reviewing the study, the reviewers will respond to the journal publisher with their recommendations, which are typically one of the following:

- **Accept for publication**. In this case, the reviewers don't see any flaws in the study, and recommend that it be published in the journal.
- **Minor revisions required**. In this case, the reviewers see minor flaws in the study, such as inadequate references in the Introduction section, minor data errors that are easily fixed, or minor omissions in the descriptions of procedures. Once these peccadilloes are fixed, the study is deemed fit for publication.
- **Major revisions required**. In this case, the reviewers see major flaws in the study requiring substantial revisions. For example, inappropriate statistical analysis, numerous errors and mismatches in data, and major

omissions in the descriptions of procedures. To make their study fit for publication, the researchers must revise their statistical analysis and rewrite portions of the paper.

- **Reject**. In this case, the reviewers find the study so poor that they deem it unacceptable for publication. For example, Introduction text that doesn't match or support the rest of the paper, highly questionable data, or unfixable flaws in design (inappropriate sample size or subject selection, for instance).

Studies can go through a number of revisions before they appear in a journal. In fact, while the peer review process has become more rapid in recent years, it's still common for studies to receive approval for publication 1 to 2 years after they were conducted.

The process of peer review provides quality control for scientific research, but like everything, it's not perfect. Every year, poor research passes peer review, sometimes because the reviewers aren't knowledgeable enough to properly review the studies or have their own biases that prevent them from being objective in their evaluation.

Some Journals Are Higher Quality Than Others

Journals can vary in the quality of the studies they tend to publish because some demand more scientific rigor than others.

The journals that tend to have higher publication standards also tend to have better reputations. For example, the *Journal of Applied Physiology* is generally considered a higher quality journal than the *Journal of Exercise Science and Fitness*.

This doesn't mean you should judge a study's quality based solely on which journal it was published in, though. Poor studies can get published even in the highest quality journals and good studies can appear in lower quality journals. Nevertheless, the journal does give you a bit of an idea of how rigorous the review process may have been for a study.

Journal Impact Factor

A journal's *impact factor* is a measure of the annual average number of citations to recent articles published in that journal. It basically answers the question, "How much does research from this particular journal get referred to by other scientists?"

The idea is that the more scientists refer to studies from a given journal in their own research, the more likely that journal is publishing high-quality studies. Thus, you can use impact factor to compare different journals in a particular line of research.

That said, while impact factor can give you a general idea of a journal's overall quality, it shouldn't be seen as a conclusive and overarching stamp of approval or disapproval. It's been criticized by many scientists for various deficiencies, and there are a number of ways for journals to artificially inflate their scores.

That said, if all of the studies on a particular topic are

published by journals with low impact factors, that can be a red flag.

How to Get Access to Journals and Studies

To read a study, you need to gain access to the journal that it's published in, and there are several ways to do this.

Here are the most common ones:

- **Your local university library (free)**. Many universities and colleges have a variety of scientific journals in their libraries, which you can visit and look up. The advantage of this method is it's free, but the disadvantages are that you need to physically travel to the university and it may or may not carry the journal you're looking for. In the latter case, you may be able to obtain it through an interlibrary loan (the university's library may be able to borrow it from another's).
- **Friends with university library access (free).** If you have friends attending a university or college, the school they're attending may have access to the journal you're looking for, so they may be able to get articles for you.
- **Open access journals (free)**. Some journals are open access, meaning anyone on the Internet can freely read their published studies. You can find a list of open access journals at doaj.org.
- **Older studies may be freely available**. Some

journals make older studies freely available online once the study is more than 1 year old.

- **ResearchGate (researchgate.net)**. A site called ResearchGate is a free social network of sorts for scientists where they can freely share their research. Not all scientists are members of ResearchGate or share their research there, and sometimes you can only access a manuscript version of the study rather than the final copy, but it's still a good resource.

- **Pay-per-view**. Many journals give you the ability to download a single journal article for a fee. This fee can vary widely from one journal to the next, ranging from as little as 5 dollars to 50 dollars or more.

- **Article Provision Services**. Services exist that give you access to multiple journals for a monthly fee. For example, DeepDyve (deepdyve.com) gives you access to a large number of journals from various publishers for a modest monthly fee. You can read as many articles as you want. However, disadvantages include being limited in how many pages you can print each month, and you have to pay extra fees if you want PDF copies of journal articles.

- **Google search**. The PDF version of the article you are looking for may be posted freely online somewhere (legally or otherwise). To find studies this way, go to Google and use the following search:"filetype:PDF *STUDY TITLE*."

The Most Popular Fitness Journals

Chances are your primary interest of research is fitness, and so below you'll find a list of some of the more recognized journals that focus solely on exercise, nutrition, or supplementation.

Exercise

Journal of Applied Physiology
Medicine and Science in Sports and Exercise
European Journal of Applied Physiology
Journal of Strength and Conditioning Research
Sports Medicine

Nutrition

American Journal of Clinical Nutrition
Journal of Nutrition
Appetite
Journal of the International Society of Sports Nutrition
International Journal of Sport Nutrition and Exercise Metabolism

Supplementation

Journal of the International Society of Sports Nutrition
International Journal of Sport Nutrition and Exercise Metabolism

There are many other lesser-known fitness journals, and studies on these topics may appear in journals that typically focus on other things. For example, nutrition studies have been published in journals such as the *Journal of the American Medical Association* and the *International Journal of Obesity*.

Nevertheless, the above list is plenty to get you started in your reading and researching.

How to Find Studies on Topics You're Interested In

There are a number of searchable online databases that index scientific studies, and the most popular one for searching studies related to health is known as PubMed. PubMed is run by the U.S. government and it has indexed the vast majority of research related to exercise, nutrition, and supplementation.

To perform a search, go to PubMed (pubmed.ncbi.nlm.nih. gov), type in the topic you want to look for in the search window, and click "Search." If you come up with too many hits to go through, you can narrow your search down using quotations, Boolean operators, or shortcodes to filter by author, year, study type, or some other variable.

You can find good tutorials on how to use its search features at fitnesssciencebook.com/pubmed.

PubMed Search Examples

Let's say you're interested in papers on muscle hypertrophy (growth). If you type in "muscle hypertrophy" in the search box, you get over 27,000 hits.

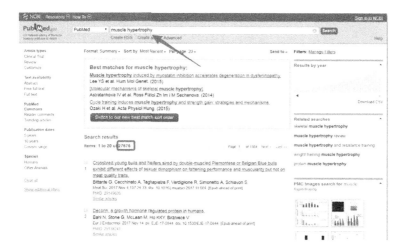

The reason you get so many hits is it's returning all articles that include *muscle* and *hypertrophy* somewhere in the paper, but not necessarily together.

The results are sorted with the most recent studies first, and you can bring more likely matches to the top by changing the sort order to the best matches by clicking "Switch to our new best match sort order." Nevertheless, 27,000+ hits is just too many to wade through. You need to narrow down your search some more.

You can narrow it down by putting "muscle hypertrophy" in quotations, which tells PubMed that you want papers with that exact phrase.

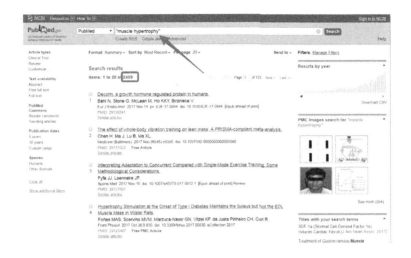

This narrows your search down to a little over 2,400 hits, which is certainly more manageable, but still a lot to sort through. Ideally, you'd narrow your search even further.

Let's say what you're specifically interested in is research on resistance training and muscle hypertrophy, in which case you could change your search to look for both phrases, like this:

As you can see, my new search string is "muscle hypertrophy" and "resistance training," separated by a space, and this yields a little over 400 hits, which will make it much easier to find papers of interest.

If you look at the left side of the screen, you see ways to filter your search even more. For example, let's say you wanted human research only, so you click the "Humans" filter on the left side.

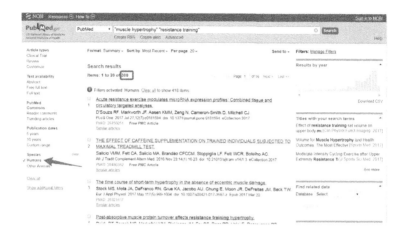

That brings the search down to a little over 300 hits, which is even better. You can activate multiple filters, so let's go further and say that you wanted human studies published in the past 5 years, so you click on the "5 years" filter next.

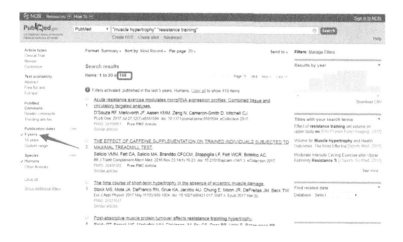

This further narrows your search down to a little over 150 hits.

You can also search for research from specific scientists. For example, Brad Schoenfeld is a well known scientist who has looked at the effects of weight training on muscle size. If you wanted to find his work, you would enter the phrase you want to search for plus Brad's last name, separated by a space, and add an [au] tag to the end of his last name, like this: "muscle hypertrophy" Schoenfeld[au] in the search box.

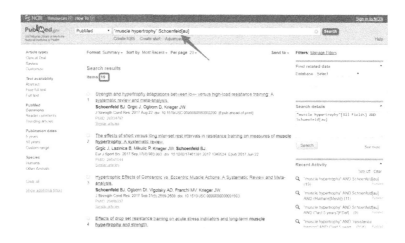

You now have 19 hits to look through.

You can also find related research by clicking on a particular study, and then clicking on "See all…" under "Similar articles" on the right hand side. For example, let's say you click on the first study in the above list of Brad Schoenfeld's publications. You'll get an abstract of the paper, and you'll see "Similar articles" on the right hand side.

Click on "See all…" on the right hand side, and you'll get 101 papers that are similar to that study.

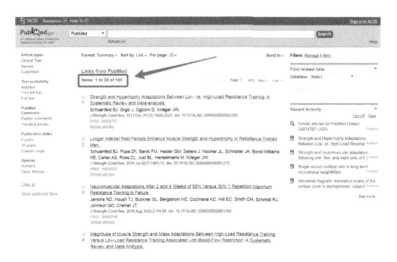

There are other filters that you can use to help narrow down your searches, but these are some of the more important and useful ones. Try experimenting yourself with different search terms, phrases, and filters, and you'll quickly grasp how to effectively use PubMed to find the research you're looking for.

Congratulations.

You've read, digested, and absorbed the foundational principles, strategies, and tactics of scientific research.

As a result, you've probably gained a whole new perspective on the realm of science, and if James and I have done our jobs well, feel more prepared than ever to find, evaluate, and apply scientific research to optimize your health, fitness, and lifestyle.

We're not done yet, though! Let's end this with a bang!

Key Takeaways

- Scientific journals are generally monthly publications that compile studies related to a particular topic.
- For a study to get published in a scientific journal, it must go through a process called peer review. Peer review involves independent scientists (typically 2 to 3) reviewing the study for flaws before it's published.
- Studies can go through a number of revisions before they appear in a journal. It's common for studies to receive approval for publication 1 to 2 years after they were conducted.
- Journals can vary in the quality of the studies they tend to publish because some demand more scientific rigor than others.
- This doesn't mean you should judge a study's quality based solely on which journal it was published in, though. Poor studies can get published even in the highest quality journals and good studies can appear in lower quality journals.
- A journal's impact factor is a measure of the annual average number of citations to recent articles published in that journal. It basically answers the question, "How much does research from this particular journal get referred to by other scientists?"
- While impact factor can give you a general idea of a journal's overall quality, it shouldn't be seen as a conclusive and overarching stamp of approval or disapproval. If all of the studies on a particular topic are published

by journals with low impact factors, though, that can be a red flag.

- There are a number of searchable online databases that index scientific studies, and the most popular one for searching studies related to health is known as PubMed. PubMed is run by the U.S. government and it has indexed the vast majority of research related to exercise, nutrition, and supplementation. You can find good tutorials on how to use its search features at fitnesssciencebook.com/pubmed.

Conclusion

*Science, my lad, is made up of mistakes, but they
are mistakes which it is useful to make, because
they lead little by little to the truth.*

—JULES VERNE

SO . . . I GUESS THIS IS IT, right? We've reached the end.

No way.

You've only learned *how to learn*, now it's time to put it into practice. It's time to take the lessons from this book and use them when you're watching videos, listening to podcasts, and reading blogs and books.

It's pretty cool to realize that you now have a set of tools that you can use to decide what's true, what isn't, and what you believe about anything related to health and fitness.

Instead of letting every new diet fad, exercise plan, and supplement send you off in the wrong direction, you can pause, evaluate the data, and come to your own conclusions.

You'll quickly find that most of what you read, see, and hear in the media about fitness is flat-out wrong, and that you're probably on the right track. Or, you may find that something you thought was true, isn't, and you need to change direction.

You win either way.

Our goal is to help you make better decisions about how you eat, train, and supplement, and I hope this book helps. There will be times when you get confused, though, which is why we want you to take one more step before you're done.

Ready? Here it is:

Fire up your favorite social media networks, announce that you've just finished the book, tell people what you thought of it, and tag me and James (our information is below), and add the #FitnessScienceExplained hashtag.

Why do this, you're wondering? Three reasons.

First, we'd love to e-meet you and help you answer any questions you have along the way.

Second, chances are some of your friends would love to learn more about this book, and this makes it easier for them to find it and learn your thoughts.

And third, by adding the hashtag, other people looking for information on the book will be able to find your post and connect with you. You can also search this hashtag on any social media platform and see what others are saying about the program. There's an entire community of people who are passionate about health and fitness research, and you're going to want to meet them.

James and I happen to be a couple of them. :-)

Here's how we can connect:

Get in touch with Mike:
- ⇒ Instagram: instagram.com/muscleforlifefitness
- ⇒ Facebook: facebook.com/muscleforlifefitness
- ⇒ Twitter: twitter.com/muscleforlife

Get in touch with James:
- ⇒ Facebook: facebook.com/james.krieger1
- ⇒ Twitter: twitter.com/weightology
- ⇒ Instagram: instagram.com/james.krieger

And last but not least, my website is legionathletics.com and James' is weightology.net, and if you want to write to me, my e-mail address is mikem@legionathletics.com, and James' is james@weightology.net.

(Keep in mind that we get a lot of emails every day, so if you can keep your message as brief as possible, it helps ensure that we can get back to everyone!)

Thanks again. We hope to hear from you, and we wish you the best!

Frequently Asked Questions

*It is the mark of an educated mind to be able to
entertain a thought without accepting it.*

—ARISTOTLE

WE'VE COVERED ALL THE MOST IMPORTANT aspects
of finding, understanding, and applying scientific research, but
you may have lingering doubts still stuck in your craw.

Let's tackle the obvious candidates here.

Why are my personal experiences sometimes at odds with what's seen in research?

There can be a number of reasons why your personal experiences may be different from what research says "should" or "shouldn't" happen.

One is natural variation in how people respond to things. Research tends to look at groups of people and then report the averages, which is highly useful, but you have to remember that this is the *average* of that group. Individual responses will vary around this average, meaning that many people will see very similar and some people will see very different results.

For example, in a study conducted by scientists at Loughborough University, people showed an average gain of about 5 percent in their quadriceps muscle after a weight training program.[1] However, the changes ranged from -2.5 percent to nearly 20 percent among the individual subjects, so while most saw results near the average of 5 percent, some actually lost muscle and some gained a large amount of muscle.

If you repeated the experiment yourself, your results may or may not be in line with the average, which might confuse you if you didn't understand why. You may even be a "non-responder," which means you won't experience *any* of the benefits seen in most other people. For example, creatine supplementation has been shown time and time again to improve strength and muscle gain, but a percentage of people that take it won't experience any gains whatsoever.[2]

Another reason your personal experiences can differ from research is your body or circumstances can be significantly different than the subjects who participated in a given study. For example, you might be a woman and a study you're reviewing involved men, or you might have been training for 20 years and the study involved people who have never done any exercise.

Things like these can be significant because factors such as gender, training experience, initial strength levels, body composition, and many others can influence the outcomes of a study. Therefore, if you're distinctly different from the types of people studied, there's a chance your experiences will differ greatly from what was observed in the study.

The differences can be even subtler, too. Let's say a study showed better muscle gains with three sets of biceps curls versus one set, and you've never seen any noticeable benefits from adding sets of curls to your regimen. What you don't know, though, is that you do a lot more pulling than the subjects in the study, which would help explain why doing additional curls doesn't help you much.

Finally, your personal experiences can be at odds with research because they represent "uncontrolled" environments, which means that other factors can be in play that weren't present in studies.

For example, let's say a study showed that a particular supplement was not beneficial for improving strength, but you swear you got stronger when you used it. Was it the supplement that caused this or was it simply the placebo effect? Or perhaps your expectation that the supplement would work subtly influenced you to train harder and pay more attention to your diet? It's impossible to completely rule out all of these possibilities without conducting proper research (and even then it can be quite difficult).

Why isn't there more research on fitness?

Performing research is very expensive, and there's only so much money to go around. Unfortunately, fitness gets very little of it because the largest funders of health research are large organizations such as the National Institute of Health (NIH), and they tend to prioritize disease and medical studies, not fitness.

In other words, most organizations think curing cancer is more important than getting bigger biceps. Our biceps might disagree, but it's probably better this way . . .

Why do fitness studies often involve so few people?

The more subjects you have, the more money your study will cost, and scientists in the fitness field usually don't have the money to do research on large numbers of people.

Why do some fitness studies tend to last for only 6 to 12 weeks?

Most fitness research is carried out at universities, and subjects are often recruited from the local student population. Thus, a duration of 6 to 12 weeks allows a study to fit into a quarter or semester at school. It can also be difficult to keep people in studies for more than three months because they're often unpaid volunteers, and thus aren't willing to make long-term commitments for the sake of a study.

Why are many of the high-quality RCTs very short in duration? Why aren't they done over longer periods of time?

When doing research on human subjects, there's a tradeoff between how much control you have over all the study variables and how long you can do the study.

For example, the most highly controlled human studies

on diet and metabolism are done in metabolic wards, where scientists have full control over the people's food intake, activity levels, and other variables. This is fantastic from a purely scientific view, but unfortunately, you generally can't keep people cooped up for longer than a week or two. Longer-term studies allow you to collect more data, but they also must be done on people in their own free-living environments, which means giving up some of the control over study variables.

How do researchers usually determine what kind of research they should do?

Most often, scientists will examine the existing research to see if there's any missing pieces that need to be filled in (what questions most need answering). Once they've decided on the questions to investigate, they need to decide how they'll go about best answering them, including whether they'll use animals or people, how the experiments will be designed and carried out, how long the study will last, what measurements they'll take, how many subjects they'll need, and many other decisions.

As you can see, a lot of thought and planning must go into a study before it even starts.

How do researchers decide if they're going to use animals or people?

This decision depends on the nature of the questions to be answered, how much control is needed over all aspects of the study, and whether they're trying to investigate underlying mechanisms or just trying to see what happens.

Animals allow for much more control and can make it easier to look at mechanisms, but the results may not necessarily apply to humans.

How do researchers decide on how many people they'll need?

To determine the number of subjects needed, scientists will do something called a *power analysis.*

This analysis begins with researchers determining the magnitude of the effect they're interested in (for example, a 10% change in muscle size). Then, they examine the results of other studies in the field to obtain information to plug into software that will, based on their inputs, estimate how many subjects will be necessary to reliably obtain the size of effect they're looking for.

How do researchers decide on what measurements they'll make?

This depends on the question that needs to be answered.

For example, if scientists want to see the impact of a diet on body fat, then they'll need to do some type of body composition assessment. If they want to see the impact of a supplement on muscle size, they'll need to do some type of measurement of muscle size (preferably a direct measurement such as ultrasound or MRI).

What does it mean if I find a study that isn't listed on PubMed?

If you can't find a study on PubMed, it usually means the study was never officially published in a journal—perhaps it was presented at a conference but never made it through peer review—or was published in a journal not indexed by PubMed.

Both of these circumstances can be red flags because if a study hasn't gone through peer review, it may be due to egregious faults or errors, and journals that aren't indexed by PubMed tend to be lower quality.

How should I think about something that only has a couple studies published on it?

You have to review the research because it really depends on the nature of the studies and various factors on the checklist.

For example, if there are just one or two studies available but they involved hundreds of people (a very large sample size) and don't contain any major errors or omissions (that you can see), then there's a good chance you should pay attention to the outcomes.

If, however, it's a couple studies of only 10 people, then you may want to be cautious in how you apply the results until more research comes out.

For instance, if a study came out on a new supplement that showed some muscle gain, that doesn't mean you should go out and start buying as much as you can. It's very possible that you'll just waste money on something that won't pan out in further research. In fact, this happened with the supplement HMB—a few early studies showed it had promise for enhancing muscle gain, but further research found it to be ineffective.

What does it mean if something works as well as placebo? Does it still work?

Something that works as well as a placebo can only "work" due to your expectations of efficacy. Because there's no true physiological mechanism behind how it's working, anything else could "work" equally well (so long as you believed it would).

For example, if I gave you a supplement that has no plausible way to increase strength but told you it would put 10 pounds on your bench press in 10 days and you believed me, this expectation alone might subtly influence your diet and training in a way that improves strength, or may even directly impact your physiology and enhance performance.

Would You Do Us a Favor?

Science does not know its debt to imagination.

—RALPH WALDO EMERSON

THANK YOU for reading our book.

We hope you enjoyed it, and we're positive that if you apply what you've learned, you'll be on your way to knowing more about the *real* science of building muscle, losing fat, and staying healthy than most people ever will.

We have a small favor to ask.

Would you mind taking a minute to write a blurb on Amazon about this book? I check all my reviews and love to get honest feedback. That's the real pay for my work—knowing that I'm helping people.

To leave a review, you can:

1. Pull up Amazon on your web browser, search for "Fitness Science Explained," click on the book, and scroll down and click on the "Write a customer review" button.

2. Visit fitnesssciencebook.com/review and you'll be automatically forwarded to Amazon to leave a review.

It doesn't have to be long, either. Even a sentence or two about what you liked most in the book or how you're going to apply it helps!

Thanks again, and we really look forward to reading your feedback!

Free Bonus Material:
Takeaways, Workout Plans, Research Reviews, and More

THANK YOU for reading *Fitness Science Explained*.

James and I hope you find it insightful, accessible, and practical, and we hope it helps you get fitter, leaner, and stronger faster.

We want to make sure you receive as much value from this book as possible, so we've put together several additional free resources to help you, including:

- A reference guide to save, share, and print, with all of this book's key takeaways, checklists, and action items.
- High-quality exercise and nutrition studies for you to analyze and interpret using the information and methods you'll learn in this book.
- "Best of" issues of the most popular fitness science research reviews, including Monthly Applications in Strength Sport (MASS), Alan Aragon's Research Review (AARR), and Weightology.

- An entire year's worth of evidence-based workouts for men and women, neatly laid out and provided in several formats, including PDF, Excel, and Google Sheets.
- And more.

To get instant access to all of those free bonuses (plus a few additional surprise gifts), go here now:

⇒ fitnesssciencebook.com/bonus

Also, if you have questions or run into difficulties, just shoot us an email at mikem@legionsupplements.com or james@weightology.net, and we'll do our best to help.

Glossary

Abstract. A high-level overview of a study that provides a summary of the purpose, methods, and findings of the study.

Anecdote. A personal account or story.

Analysis of Variance (ANOVA). A type of statistical procedure for analyzing three or more groups.

Bell Curve. A bell curve, also called a *normal distribution*, is a function that represents the distribution of many variables according to their standard deviation around the mean. Data graphed as a normal distribution will have a large rounded peak tapering away at each end, so that it's shaped like a bell.

Cherry Picking. Selectively choosing data that confirms a hypothesis while ignoring data that disagrees with that hypothesis.

Cohort. A group of subjects that's followed over time.

Cohort Study. A study where a single group (cohort) or multiple groups of subjects (cohorts) are followed over time, ranging from a number of days to many years.

Competing Interest. Anything that interferes with, or could be perceived as interfering with, an objective presentation, article, or study.

Conclusion. A summary of the most important findings of a study, and how those findings may be applied.

Confidence Interval. A range of values that contains a specified probability of the true (perfectly accurate) value of a given parameter.

Confounding Variable. A variable that may affect the outcome that you're studying and lead to incorrect conclusions about the relationships you're looking at.

Control Group. A group that receives no treatment or some type of "usual" or "standard of care" treatment.

Correlation. A mutual relationship between two variables.

Crossover Study. A study design where subjects receive more than one treatment during the study.

Cross-Sectional Study. An observational study where you compare two different groups at a specific point in time.

Discussion. The section of a study where the researchers talk about their results and what they mean, as well as the study's strengths and limitations.

Double-Blind. A study where neither the subjects nor the researchers know who's getting which treatment.

Effect Size. A measurement used to represent the magnitude of a change.

External Validity. The ability to generalize the results of a study to other situations.

Falsification. A process of testing a hypothesis against data, and finding that the data doesn't support the hypothesis.

Impact Factor. A measure of the annual average number of citations to recent articles published in a journal. It basically answers the question, "How much does research from this particular journal get referred to by other scientists?"

Independent Variable. The variable in an experiment that you change on purpose.

Inference. A conclusion based on a set of data or body of evidence.

Introduction. The section of a study where the researchers introduce the problem or question that needs to be answered, and explain why they did the study.

In Vitro Study. A study where scientists look at the effects of something outside its natural environment, as in a test tube or cell culture. (Latin for "in glass").

Hierarchy of Evidence. A framework for ranking pieces of evidence based on their type.

Hypothesis. A proposed explanation for a problem or set of observations.

Limitation. A characteristic of a study that can influence and limit the interpretation of the findings.

Matched. A method in research of pairing every subject in a particular group with an equivalent subject in another group, to ensure the groups are as similar as possible.

Mean. An average value for a group.

Meta-Analysis. A statistical analysis of a group of studies on a particular topic.

Metabolic Ward. A hospital-like setting where subjects are housed during a study, and where precise measurements of diet, physical activity, and energy expenditure can be made.

Methods. The section of a study where the researchers describe what they did.

Narrative Review. An article where a researcher or researchers will informally gather evidence around a topic and share their opinions about what it means.

Non-Parametric Statistics. A category of statistics that doesn't assume the data is distributed in a normal fashion or bell curve.

Observational Study. A study where scientists observe people in their free-living environment, collect data on them, and then look for relationships between variables that the scientists are interested in.

Parametric Statistics. A category of statistics that assumes that data has been taken from a larger data set that falls along a normal distribution or bell curve.

Peer Review. A process where scientists review the work of other scientists before a study is published.

Placebo. An inert or "do-nothing" substance or treatment given to subjects in a study.

Population. All elements, individuals, or units that meet the selection criteria for a group to be studied.

Prediction. An outcome or observation that should hold true if a particular hypothesis is true.

Prospective Study. A study where scientists decide what they are going to do, start collecting data, and then analyze it at some point in the future.

PubMed. A public search index of medical and health studies.

P-Value. A probability value meant to represent how likely the findings of a study are due to random chance.

Randomized. A study where subjects are randomly assigned to the various treatments.

Randomized Controlled Trial. A type of study where scientists take a group of people or animals and divide them into two or more groups in a random fashion. The scientists will try to keep everything the same between the groups, except for one variable which will be the variable to be investigated. One group will be a "do nothing" or "sham" group, known as the control group.

Replication. The repetition of a scientific experiment or trial to obtain a consistent result.

Reproducibility. The ability of an entire experiment to be duplicated, either by the same researcher or by independent scientists.

Results. The section of a study where the scientists describe what they found.

Retrospective Study. A study where scientists collect data on things that have already happened, and then analyze it to look for important relationships and outcomes.

Sample. A portion drawn from a population, the study of which is intended to lead to statistical estimates of the attributes of the whole population.

Sample Size. The number of subjects or animals in a study.

Science. The systematic study of the structure and behavior of the physical and natural world through observation and experiment.

Scientific Journal. A recurring publication, often monthly, that contains published scientific research.

Single-Blind. A study where either the subjects or the researchers don't know what type of treatment the subjects received, but not both.

Standard Deviation (SD). A measure of how "spread out" the data is in a group, and specifically how spread out it is around the mean of the group.

Standard Error (SE or SEM). A measure of how closely the "true" average of an entire population was estimated.

Statistical Analysis. A group of formal methods for examining data, and drawing conclusions from that data.

Statistical Significance. A condition where the P-value is below a certain pre-specified level. It is often used to determine the likelihood that an outcome is due to chance.

Systematic Review. A type of literature review that involves gathering all of the research on a particular topic, and then evaluating it based on a predefined set of criteria and rules.

Theory. A well-supported explanation for a set of observations that has withstood rigorous data collection, testing, and experimentation.

T-Test. A type of statistical procedure for comparing two groups. An independent t-test is where you compare the average of two distinctly different groups, while a paired t-test is where you compare two measurements from the same group (like before and after a diet or training program).

Type I Error. A false positive result (a result demonstrating positive effect when, in reality, there was none).

Type II Error. A false negative result (a result demonstrating no effect when, in reality, there was one).

Washout Period. A period of time between treatments to allow any residual effects of one treatment to disappear before you give another one.

Weight of the Evidence. A measure of the amount of evidence on one side of an issue or problem compared to the amount of evidence on the other side.

Endnotes

Chapter One

[1] Greenwood DC, Threapleton DE, Evans CEL, et al. Association between sugar-sweetened and artificially sweetened soft drinks and type 2 diabetes: Systematic review and dose-response meta-analysis of prospective studies. Br J Nutr. 2014;112(5):725-734. doi:10.1017/S0007114514001329

[2] Miller PE, Perez V. Low-calorie sweeteners and body weight and composition: A meta-analysis of randomized controlled trials and prospective cohort studies. Am J Clin Nutr. 2014;100(3):765-777. doi:10.3945/ajcn.113.082826

3   Selvaraj S, Borkar DS, Prasad V. Media Coverage of Medical Journals: Do the Best Articles Make the News? Gong Y, ed. PLoS One. 2014;9(1):e85355. doi:10.1371/journal.pone.0085355

4   Dolinsky VW, Jones KE, Sidhu RS, et al. Improvements in skeletal muscle strength and cardiac function induced by resveratrol during exercise training contribute to enhanced exercise performance in rats. J Physiol. 2012;590(11):2783-2799. doi:10.1113/jphysiol.2012.230490

5   Freedman ND, Park Y, Abnet CC, Hollenbeck AR, Sinha R. Association of Coffee Drinking with Total and Cause-Specific Mortality. N Engl J Med. 2012;366(20):1891-1904. doi:10.1056/NEJMoa1112010

6   Morenga L Te, Mallard S, Mann J. Dietary sugars and body weight: Systematic review and meta-analyses of randomised controlled trials and cohort studies. BMJ. 2013;345(7891). doi:10.1136/bmj.e7492

7   Rogers PJ, Brunstrom JM. Appetite and energy balancing. Physiol Behav. 2016;164:465-471. doi:10.1016/j.physbeh.2016.03.038

8   Lowery RP, Joy JM, Rathmacher JA, et al. Interaction
     of beta-hydroxy-beta-methylbutyrate free acid and
     adenosine triphosphate on muscle mass, strength,
     and power in resistance trained individuals. J Strength
     Cond Res. 2016;30(7):1843-1854. doi:10.1519/
     JSC.0000000000000482

9   Durkalec-Michalski K, Jeszka J. The effect of β-hy-
     droxy-β-methylbutyrate on aerobic capacity and
     body composition in trained athletes. J Strength
     Cond Res. 2016;30(9):2617-2626. doi:10.1519/
     JSC.0000000000001361

10   Soffritti M, Belpoggi F, Degli Esposti D, Lambertini
     L. Original Studies/Studi Originali General Topics/
     Argomenti Generali Aspartame Induces Lymphomas
     and Leukaemias in Rats a L'aspartame Induce Linfomi e
     Leucemie Nei Ratti. Vol 10.; 2005.

11   Wakefield AJ, Murch SH, Anthony A, et al. Retracted:
     Ileal-lymphoid-nodular hyperplasia, non-specific
     colitis, and pervasive developmental disorder in chil-
     dren. Lancet. 1998;351(9103):637-641. doi:10.1016/
     S0140-6736(97)11096-0

[12]   Meng H, Matthan NR, Ausman LM, Lichtenstein AH. Effect of macronutrients and fiber on postprandial glycemic responses and meal glycemic index and glycemic load value determinations. Am J Clin Nutr. 2017;105(4):842-853. doi:10.3945/ajcn.116.144162

Chapter Two

[1]   Kersten S. Mechanisms of nutritional and hormonal regulation of lipogenesis. EMBO Rep. 2001;2(4):282. doi:10.1093/EMBO-REPORTS/KVE071

[2]   Jensen MD, Haymond MW, Rizza RA, Cryer PE, Miles JM. Influence of body fat distribution on free fatty acid metabolism in obesity. J Clin Invest. 1989;83(4):1168-1173. doi:10.1172/JCI113997

[3]   Rebelos E, Muscelli E, Natali A, et al. Body weight, not insulin sensitivity or secretion, may predict spontaneous weight changes in nondiabetic and prediabetic subjects: The RISC study. Diabetes. 2011;60(7):1938-1945. doi:10.2337/db11-0217

[4]   Hall KD. A review of the carbohydrate-insulin model of obesity. Eur J Clin Nutr. 2017;71(3):323-326. doi:10.1038/ejcn.2016.260

5   Gofman JW, Lindgren F, Elliott H, et al. The role of
     lipids and lipoproteins in atherosclerosis. Science (80-).
     1950;111(2877). doi:10.1126/science.111.2877.166

6   Tariq SM, Sidhu MS, Toth PP, Boden WE. HDL hypoth-
     esis: Where do we stand now? Curr Atheroscler Rep.
     2014;16(4):398. doi:10.1007/s11883-014-0398-0

7   Heyward VH. Evaluation of body composition.
     Current issues. Sport Med. 1996;22(3):146-156.
     doi:10.2165/00007256-199622030-00002

8   Schoenfeld BJ, Ogborn D, Krieger JW. Dose-response
     relationship between weekly resistance training volume
     and increases in muscle mass: A systematic review and
     meta-analysis. J Sports Sci. 2017;35(11):1073-1082. doi:10.
     1080/02640414.2016.1210197

9   R Y, V K, RJ C, et al. Using biomarker data to adjust
     estimates of the distribution of usual intakes for misre-
     porting: application to energy intake in the US popula-
     tion [corrected] [published erratum appears in J AM
     DIET ASSOC 2008 May;108(5):890]. J Am Diet Assoc.
     2008;108(3):455-464. doi:http://dx.doi.org/10.1016/j.
     jada.2007.12.004

[10] Warner ET, Wolin KY, Duncan DT, Heil DP, Askew S, Bennett GG. Differential accuracy of physical activity self-report by body mass index. Am J Health Behav. 2012;36(2):168-178. doi:10.5993/AJHB.36.2.3

Chapter Three

[1] Gosnell BA, Mitchell JE, Lancaster KL, Burgard MA, Wonderlich SA, Crosby RD. Food presentation and energy intake in a feeding laboratory study of subjects with binge eating disorder. Int J Eat Disord. 2001;30(4):441-446. doi:10.1002/eat.1105

[2] Schoenfeld BJ, Grgic J, Ogborn D, Krieger JW. Strength and hypertrophy adaptations between low- vs. High-load resistance training: A systematic review and meta-analysis. J Strength Cond Res. 2017;31(12):3508-3523. doi:10.1519/JSC.0000000000002200

[3] Vickers AJ, Cronin AM, Maschino AC, et al. Acupuncture for chronic pain: Individual patient data meta-analysis. Arch Intern Med. 2012;172(19):1444-1453. doi:10.1001/archinternmed.2012.3654

Chapter Four

[1]   Fink J, Schoenfeld BJ, Kikuchi N, Nakazato K. Effects of drop set resistance training on acute stress indicators and long-term muscle hypertrophy and strength. J Sports Med Phys Fitness. 2018;58(5):597-605. doi:10.23736/S0022-4707.17.06838-4

[2]   Philip Karl J, Meydani M, Barnett JB, et al. Substituting whole grains for refined grains in a 6-wk randomized trial favorably affects energy-balance metrics in healthy men and postmenopausal women1-3. Am J Clin Nutr. 2017;105(3):589-599. doi:10.3945/ajcn.116.139683

[3]   Lexchin J, Bero LA, Djulbegovic B, Clark O. Pharmaceutical industry sponsorship and research outcome and quality: Systematic review. Br Med J. 2003;326(7400):1167-1170. doi:10.1136/bmj.326.7400.1167

[4]   Krieger JW, Crowe M, Blank SE. Chronic glutamine supplementation increases nasal but not salivary IgA during 9 days of interval training. J Appl Physiol. 2004;97(2):585-591. doi:10.1152/japplphysiol.00971.2003

[5]   Kesselheim AS, Robertson CT, Myers JA, et al. A Randomized Study of How Physicians Interpret Research Funding Disclosures. N Engl J Med. 2012;367(12):1119-1127. doi:10.1056/NEJMsa1202397

6   Schoenfeld BJ, Ogborn D, Krieger JW. Dose-response relationship between weekly resistance training volume and increases in muscle mass: A systematic review and meta-analysis. J Sports Sci. 2017;35(11):1073-1082. doi:10.1080/02640414.2016.1210197

7   Hass CJ, Garzarella L, De Hoyos D, Pollock ML. Single versus multiple sets in long-term recreational weight-lifters. Med Sci Sports Exerc. 2000;32(1):235-242. doi:10.1097/00005768-200001000-00035

8   Marshall PWM, McEwen M, Robbins DW. Strength and neuromuscular adaptation following one, four, and eight sets of high intensity resistance exercise in trained males. Eur J Appl Physiol. 2011;111(12):3007-3016. doi:10.1007/s00421-011-1944-x

Chapter Six

1   Phillips BE, Williams JP, Greenhaff PL, Smith K, Atherton PJ. Physiological adaptations to resistance exercise as a function of age. JCI insight. 2017;2(17). doi:10.1172/jci.insight.95581

[2]   Lowery RP, Joy JM, Rathmacher JA, et al. Interaction of beta-hydroxy-beta-methylbutyrate free acid and adenosine triphosphate on muscle mass, strength, and power in resistance trained individuals. J Strength Cond Res. 2016;30(7):1843-1854. doi:10.1519/JSC.0000000000000482

[3]   Durkalec-Michalski K, Jeszka J. The effect of β-hydroxy-β-methylbutyrate on aerobic capacity and body composition in trained athletes. J Strength Cond Res. 2016;30(9):2617-2626. doi:10.1519/JSC.0000000000001361

[4]   Dieter BP, Schoenfeld BJ, Aragon AA. The data do not seem to support a benefit to BCAA supplementation during periods of caloric restriction. J Int Soc Sports Nutr. 2016;13(1). doi:10.1186/s12970-016-0128-9

FAQ

[1]   Erskine RM, Jones DA, Williams AG, Stewart CE, Degens H. Inter-individual variability in the adaptation of human muscle specific tension to progressive resistance training. Eur J Appl Physiol. 2010;110(6):1117-1125. doi:10.1007/s00421-010-1601-9

2   Cooper R, Naclerio F, Allgrove J, Jimenez A. Creatine
supplementation with specific view to exercise/sports
performance: An update. J Int Soc Sports Nutr. 2012;9:33.
doi:10.1186/1550-2783-9-33

Made in the USA
Columbia, SC
02 April 2021